A 40-YEAR TREASURY

40 Years of Bob Livingston

A Special Digest of Priceless Wisdom and Knowledge From *The Bob Livingston Letter*

By Bob Livingston
Founder, *Personal Liberty Alerts*
Editor, *The Bob Livingston Letter*

Published by *The Bob Livingston Letter*
P.O. Box 3623, Hueytown, AL 35023
www.BobLivingstonLetter.com
www.PersonalLiberty.com

40 Years of Bob Livingston

A Special Digest of Priceless Wisdom
and Knowledge From
The Bob Livingston Letter

Contents

A Special Digest of Priceless Wisdom and Knowledge From *The Bob Livingston Letter*

More than 40 years ago, Bob Livingston saw where the nation and the world was headed, and he was alarmed. He knew he had to speak up, to be the warning oracle for those who would hear and heed the alarm. He launched *The Bob Livingston Letter* to expose the lies, deceit, misinformation, and disinformation being spread as "truth" by the government, the manipulated media, and the controlling elite.

In the decades or so since, contrarian Bob Livingston has stood vigilant as a sometimes lonely, but always a steadfast and vocal sentinel against the forces from within and from without our country that seek to subvert our freedoms and control our lives for their own ends. He has never let down his guard against those who would rob us of our hard-earned wealth or sap our precious health to make us more docile and controllable.

Readers of *The Bob Livingston Letter* over the years have been forewarned of dangers to avoid and opportunities to seize in both health and wealth matters. In thousands of pages published in the past 40-plus years, Bob Livingston shared wisdom and knowledge that has consistently proven to be priceless to his readers.

We have sifted through the rich treasury of powerful ideas, advice, tips, insights, and perspectives contained in past volumes of *The Bob Livingston Letter* to compile this special digest of the BEST health and wealth wisdom from the collection.

Read, learn, heed, and act.

Pearls of Wisdom From
The Bob Livingston Letter

★ Gold is the substance of economic survival. It is the essence of privacy and the preservation of wealth.

★ Currencies are not money but symbols of money.

★ Self-deception and denial is the social mood in a mania. The crowd can literally feed on hot air without any consideration whatsoever of the facts and reality. The crowd is predictable and so are politicians and governments that host upon the public mind.

★ Government will never investigate itself.

★ Human liberty and personal survival in our time must originate in truth no matter how incredible or shocking to our conditioned minds. Governments control the public mind with disinformation and confusion. No modern government could exist for 24 hours if it told people the truth.

★ Survival is privacy, and privacy is survival.

★ When money supply is increased, there is not an increase in actual wealth. Just the opposite, new money is negative wealth. It destroys the wealth of the people and transfers it to the money creators.

★ All speculative manias in history have led to financial excesses, overproduction capacities, and huge debt. This has led to a vicious downturn and financial busts, which in turn has led to recessions or depressions. The very salient point is that none of the financial establishment or public gurus saw the collapse coming now or in the past.

★ So-called "modern medicine" is a commercial whore sitting upon the bodies of untold millions of murdered people who were treated with a false paradigm.

★ Prosperity finally consumes itself on debt and overproduction.

★ Awareness by itself is the foundation of freedom.

★ Modern medicine is proof enough that modern man is more than ever a victim of superstition and witchcraft.

★ We tend to forget that the alchemists who have made us believe that abstract numbers on pieces of paper is money, still have not found a way to manufacture gold.

CHAPTER 1

Bob Livingston's Philosophy

The difference in people is how they think. The difference in what people think is what they read. The difference in what they read is how much they read. How much they read is how close to reality they are.

It is so planned that billions of people should "live" and die and never know or experience reality. The crowd can be described with one word—frivolous. The people are little children whose existence is prescribed by the system.

Yes, our parameters of existence are prescribed because our parameters of thought are prescribed.

Who are the people of the system? They are almost everybody. They are the common folk. They are the professional class. They are for the most part, the financial class.

A few get through the net to reality. And most people who climb the economic scale are decoyed and diverted with materialism. Their existence becomes totally dominated by the desire to accumulate material wealth.

Riches are wonderful. They please the flesh, but they are a blinder that most often blocks escape to reality. Materialism properly placed brings balance and quality time to life. Materialism is a tool, not an end, lest we worship at the altar of mammon.

There is an appalling difference between reality people and people of the system. Frivolous people have their existence on frivolous thoughts and frivolous talk.

The system prescribes how we live and how we die with few exceptions. My focus is on health and wealth—properly balanced. It is impossible to have one without the other.

Good health is where you can find it. It is seldom found within the sickness system or "orthodox medicine." It is most likely to be found in alternatives.

People can be measured by their proclivity toward alternative health. This is the same as saying their disbelief of pharmaceutical medicine. The more we progress to alternative health the closer we come to reality.

Pharmaceutical medicine is by no definition a health system. It is in every way a commercial business based on profits. Not one doctor in 10,000 suspects this. So tight is the psychological control of the medical system, that no amount of persuasion or logic can dislodge it.

The professional medical class is money motivated and they lust after the pharmaceutical system, totally unconscious of the realism of human health. A drug system is incompatible with the health of man and animal.

Wealth is long-term value. It most definitely is not the diminishing, deflating paper money system that everyone thinks of as money and wealth.

Silently, a new war has been declared on all people who hold paper money assets. The paper money monster called depreciating paper is consuming more and more while we sleep.

Again, to the extent that we recognize the fraud and immoral nature of depreciating paper money, to this extent we escape into reality. He who builds his fortune, his savings, and retirement upon a paper money foundation builds his house upon the sands.

This syndrome is no different from the drug addict who plans his existence upon acquiring the next fix. Think on transferring your existence from pharmaceutical drugs and paper money to life and reality above the "madness of the crowd" while you can.

Be Prepared

If we can't visualize a storm in fair weather it is too late when the clouds appear. Likewise, people who can't imagine hunger never store food.

People fend off a life insurance salesman saying that they don't need life insurance. Of course they don't! If they needed it, it would be too late.

What foolish irresponsibility human nature is. We Americans "educated" in public schools (government schools) are conditioned to respond to the prescribed parameters of thought.

Anything outside of the system of thought seems like heresy. Translated, this means that the population embraces and protects the system that controls, enslaves, and eventually destroys it.

Perception must become perspective before it becomes commonplace. This means that we as advanced thinkers must see the potential ending of political and financial maneuvering before the crowd does.

The Threshold of Intelligence: What is it?

The threshold of intelligence is the conscious level of thought. The threshold of intelligence is being suppressed/reduced all the time. In and at this level there is no original, creative, or analytical thought.

Governments fear a rising threshold of intelligence, hence public schools. The lower the conscious reality the easier people are to control.

The answer for you to rise above the crowd is to be a consistent reader of quality material. The more that you put in your mental computer, the more and higher level you can compute and create.

All great men and women are avid readers. That is why they are achievers. If you are too busy to read, you are too busy.

It is shocking how few people read. It's as if they repulse

Continued on page 15.

Does Bob Livingston Have a Crystal Ball?

For more than 40 years, *The Bob Livingston Letter* has been so right so often in its predictions that readers might wonder if Bob has some magic help to foresee and foretell the future. Many of his predictions have contradicted what "everyone says" and have been so outrageous and far-fetched according to the "conventional wisdom" of the time that they seemed unbelievable. That is, until time and events proved them to be true!

No, Bob Livingston doesn't have a crystal ball or any other magic aid that mystically opens the window of time and gives him a privileged view of tomorrow. What he does possess is acute common sense and a clear-headed view of the world untainted by propaganda from the government and the controlled media.

Bob Livingston sees the facts as they really are, not as the mind-manipulators would have us see them. He considers these facts with an individualist mind free of the collective bias. He sees clearly the path where the facts lead and follows it to the logical conclusion. And he has the courage and conviction to state the conclusion unequivocally, whether it is comfortable to the public or not.

In recent years, readers of *The Bob Livingston Letter* learned long before everyone else of some of the most dramatic developments of our time:

Y2K

At the beginning of 1999, public awareness and concern about the Y2K computer "bug" that many feared would result in global catastrophe was rapidly escalating into panic. But *The Bob Livingston Letter,* while acknowledging there might be some risk, cautioned not to get stampeded by the Y2K hype.

"Believe me, there is a lot of hype out there about Y2K. 1999 promises to be a Y2Krazy year. We have talked to people who have already spent thousands of dollars for all sorts of things. Motivation based on fear hysteria leads to serious mistakes in judgment.

"Basic preparation, we think, is rational. The ideal is to get those things and do those things for basic survival for a few weeks. But get things that you can later consume or use. People are buying vast amounts of storage supplies that will accumulate dust and never be used." —*The Bob Livingston Letter,* January 1999

(In a later issue, when the Y2K paranoia had reached a frenzy, Bob said, "Since I have been personally prepared for general emergencies for 40 years, I have not been concerned with Y2K preparations.")

Dollar Decline, End of the Stock Market Boom, Beginning of Gold Bull Market

Also early in 1999, the stock market mania was in the 17th year of the longest bull in history and "irrational exuberance" made everybody a tycoon investor. Washington and Wall Street trumpeted the age of perpetual prosperity for all. Gold had been in a 20-year slide since its peak at $800 in 1980. But Bob Livingston prophesied some dramatic surprises ahead:

"As interest rates go down, the dollar will head south. A weak dollar is always positive for gold. Gold and the dollar move in opposite directions.

"We are still in a financial asset mania. The stock market is topping and the gold market is bottoming. With this extreme between financial assets and tangible assets, we should not be far from visible signs of reversal.

"Most holders of gold stocks are very discouraged, but if you sell now you will be selling at the bottom."

— *The Bob Livingston Letter,* January 1999

Bob was way ahead of the curve—calling the reversals in the dollar, the stock market, and gold almost two years before they materialized. He continually repeated the alarms in issue after issue. The accuracy of the predictions was dead on target, but only the most courageous and honest thinkers would believe they could be true.

"Nothing rises or falls forever. The bullish consensus data shows that currency traders are extremely bullish on the U.S. dollar. This by itself is a sign of the end for the dollar.

"The dollar is over-owned by everybody... 78 percent of the world's central bank reserves are in U.S. dollars. There is a dollar firestorm coming as the Federal Reserve rushes to lower interest rates.

"A collapsing dollar means a collapsing stock market and a new birth for gold." —*The Bob Livingston Letter,* January 2001

King Dollar began slipping from its throne as the world's dominant currency in February 2002 and has lost 23 percent of its value since. The stock market peaked in January 2000 (though few investors could believe the bubble had actually already burst) and has lost $8 trillion in share value in the long bear market slide since then. Gold reversed course in April 2001 and launched a long-term major bullish trend that could run for another eight to ten years. Gold stocks leveraged to physical gold prices have become respectable again... and have performed handsomely.

The Corporate Scandal Outbreak

In February 2001, eight months before the Enron scandal darkened Wall Street and tipped over a string of dominoes that included WorldCom, IMClone, Martha Stewart, and a host of others, Bob warned: "There are at least four bubbles in the U.S. economy that I know of. There is the over investment in capital spending, the U.S. dollar bubble, the stock market bubble, and the huge stock option bubble.

"The last has not surfaced yet but I think that it promises to be a scandal involving almost the whole of American big business. Business is creating assets with paper, paying employees with them, taking tax deductions, and they are disappearing with the crashing stock market. This thing is screaming for exposure!"

—*The Bob Livingston Letter,* February 2001

The accuracy of predictions published in *The Bob Livingston Letter* since 1969 has made believers of long-time readers... even when the predictions seem improbable. Who needs a crystal ball when you have *The Bob Livingston Letter?*

Continued from page 11.

reading. I can talk with a person a very few minutes and I can tell if they are serious readers. By far most of the people that I talk with disappoint. It is so sad because so much awaits us!

Reading translates you into reality so that you don't believe in myths. Reading helps you to escape the fraud of politics and bureaucracy. Reading helps you to compress time.

A reader experiences many exciting lifetimes. A reader is his/her own best friend.

In an un-free and crisis world there is mental freedom aplenty. Reading shatters anxiety about world events and makes for emotional stability.

There is time for other things. I talk to and hug my dogs every day! I read four to six books a month.

Currently I'm reading or re-reading *The Fat Resistance Diet,* by Dr. Leo Galland; *How to Hide Anything,* by Michael Connor; *Trust Us, We're Experts,* (about how industry manipulates science and gambles with your future) by Sheldon Rampton and John Stauber; *Propaganda,* by Edward Bernays; *Manufacturing Consent,* by Edward S. Herman and Noam Chomsky; *Good-bye Germ Theory,* by Dr. William P. Trebing; *Rethinking Pasteur's Germ Theory,* by Nancy Appleton; and *The Miracle of Magnesium,* by Carolyn Dean M.D., N.D.

I subscribe to many health and financial newsletters that cost about $15,000 per year. My forte is health and wealth. Won't you join me for a better life?

I am totally excited even as the world shatters about me. I can survive because I have read thousands of books and newsletters. Books and newsletters don't cost, they pay and they pay big!

What Does the U.S. Have That No Other Nation Has Ever Had?

The answer is extradition treaties and mutual legal assistance treaties.

Included in this is the forcible abduction of a "fugitive" who is brought to the U.S. by force and tried. Remember, Panama's Noriega is now in a Miami jail for several years.

Also, Adolph Eichmann was abducted from Argentina by Israel (same as U.S.), tried in Israel, and executed.

It is a fact that many nations try to protect political fugitives but U.S. power can intimidate them in many ways to surrender fugitives under some pretext. The Mutual Legal Assistance Treaty (MLAT) is used to get financial records and any other personal information from nations outside the U.S.

The U.S. has only to demonstrate "probable cause." Probable cause is an umbrella for abuses by all sorts of police Gestapos. Probable cause carries the color of law that can be translated into anything.

Mutual Legal Assistance Treaties cover the globe and expedite the prosecution of transnational crime. Many people are not aware that the U.S. Government administers an extensive world empire with extradition and MLAT. Even these treaties are a cover and a pretense for universal force.

I have written in the past about a concept that we created and named Benevolent Totalitarianism. Of course these terms create an oxymoron or contradiction. But they describe international lawlessness with a pretty face.

This is another way to commit crime in the name of justice. Have all of you read *The Prince,* by Machievella? In other words, tyrants cover their asses with legal fictions that keep the crowd sedated. They always operate from an "Ivory Tower" to maintain trust and credibility.

U.S. tax law for private persons is a world class example of forcing mass conformity with witchcraft written in legal mumbo jumbo that nobody can understand. Even the "enforcers" don't have a clue.

Should we say crime created with fiction and doublethink backed by force? *The Bob Livingston Letter* is written for information only. We advocate obeying all laws of the land.

Ignorance of Reality

The system and its controlled masses are hostile toward reality. They want no discomfort of thought. They are at peace with regimentation although not aware.

The system is pabulum for lazy people. The first wakeup call is to come to know that there is a system. The system is public education, including colleges and the universities. It is two political parties that are the same except in name. It is the controlled media. It is the medical system. It is fiat or paper money.

The purpose of the system is to control the people so that most of what we think about and talk about is noise. But there is enough information for those who read to separate fact from fiction. It takes some a few years and others a lifetime.

People mimic the system because they don't have enough information to process or separate fact from fiction or to know reality. The system permanently insulates most people from reality. There is no hope for them unless they seek reality regardless of their inbred convictions.

Those who do read regularly and seek information usually progress with others of like mind. IQ, educational, or professional background or even financial success in no way provides a special escape hatch from the entrapment of "the system."

Unless one escapes the parameters of the system it will, one way or the other, distort our perception of reality. And as long as we are mentally encumbered by "the system" we are subject to being manipulated against our best interest.

The very best example that I can think of is Warren Buffett. Mr. Buffett's favorite causes are legalized abortion and population control. And he is giving billions to support these establishment issues. He is not thinking his own thoughts on these issues but the thoughts of "the system." He is confusing altruism with reality.

So here is a financial genius whose wealth is shot in the void. Legalized abortion (murder) and population control even if they were not moral issues, are inconsistent with human liberty which is the very basis of Mr. Buffett's fortune. Even if we call them political issues they were basic to national socialism, again anathema to Mr. Buffett's free enterprise.

People with system blinders on cannot see the axiom that, "things that are equal to the same thing are equal to each other." If there are two politicians each under different party labels but upon objective analysis they have the same philosophy and the approximate voting record, they are the same in reality.

An inconsistent mind knows not the difference in system-taught altruism and the sour odor of fraud upon the people and himself which the emperors upon the thrones of the earth created.

The Business of the U.S. is War

The military budget of Russia is $24.9 billion annually. China's budget is $35.3 billion. India's military budget is $22.4 billion. The UK's military budget is $57.8 billion. France's is $55.4 billion. The U.S. military budget is a whopping $560 billion annually.

What is Your Perception of Reality?

Answer these questions... My answers are below each question:

1. **The U.S. dollar became 100 percent fiat currency in 1971. Should I hold all my assets in the U.S. dollar, a depreciating currency?** *Answer:* If you are holding your assets in U.S. dollars, your assets are melting, causing big losses.

2. **Do prices go up, called inflation, or is the dollar becoming worth less because the central bank is printing so much paper money?** *Answer:* People think of rising prices as inflation but in reality rising prices means depreciating paper money.

3. **Are the Republican and Democratic Party two separate parties?** *Answer:* The Republican and Democratic Parties are one and the same under different names. Both promote big government vs. the individual.

4. **Can the word democracy be a front for gradually developing fascism?** *Answer:* Democracy is a front for fast developing fascism. Hitler called his Nazism a great democracy.

5. **Would the U.S. Government promote adulterated food as clean and wholesome?** *Answer:* The government not only promotes adulterated food, they enforce the consumption of the same by refusing alternative health foods access to the public. (More on this subject can be found in the Health section)

6. **Does the U.S. Government owe money?** *Answer:* The U.S. Government owes no money because there is no money of account in the U.S.

7. **Has the Iraq War cost any money?** *Answer:* The Iraq war cost nothing. There is only pretended payment with created credit.

8. **Was or is there a difference in Communism and Nazism?** *Answer:* No difference between Communism and Nazism, only the names. In both the state is supreme.

9. **When national identities have different names, does that mean they are different?** *Answer:* No, same as above.

10. **Do you own some gold and silver coins?** *Answer:* If you own gold and silver coins, you are ahead of the crowd. You are seeing your wealth increase.

11. **Do you read only establishment press?** *Answer:* If you read only establishment press, you have thought-control by the state.

12. **Do you believe that governments hold political, economic, and spiritual power through deception?** *Answer:* Governments hold all power through deception.

13. **Do you believe that synthetic or chemical man-made foods are healthy?** *Answer:* Man-made synthetic or processed foods are very negative for health.

14. **Do you believe that in time the consumption of fructose corn syrup will make every person in the population diabetic?** *Answer:* Fructose corn syrup is a synthetic sweetener which bypasses the pancreas, in time causing diabetes.

15. **Why do you think that the government does not warn**

against fructose corn syrup the same as it does terrorism?
Answer: The government allows fructose corn syrup so therefore they promote it. It is a nonfood that is dangerous to health.

16. **Is "public health" actually public health?** *Answer:* Public health is really public sickness with a very high price tag. The U.S. is number one in cost and number 72 in "health care."

17. **What is the basic difference between the philosophy of free enterprise and socialism?** *Answer:* Free enterprise promotes the individual, Socialism promotes the state.

18. **Is wealth and the ownership of paper money the same?** *Answer:* Wealth is not paper money. Paper money destroys wealth.

19. **Do you believe that you can be manipulated with propaganda?** *Answer:* Propaganda manipulates the people against their best interest.

20. **Which powerful vitamin is anti-cancer according to massive but not known research?** *Answer:* Vitamin D3 is a most powerful vitamin/hormone and very anti-cancer.

Federal Debt?
(For the Benefit of New Subscribers)

I read a lot of intelligent writers who believe that there is a Federal Government debt. They believe that the U.S. Government owes trillions of dollars. If you had a printing press with a monopoly to print any amount of money, would you owe any money?

Not only this, the U.S. Government printing press monopoly is backed by military force to make sure nobody else prints money. They also have legal tender laws that force the public to accept their paper money. What a deal!

The Iraqi War is a paper money war as are all modern wars. Do you think that there would be wars if they had to be paid for in gold?

Then why the income tax? Good question and I have an excellent answer. The income tax system is a mind machine.

The people have been "educated" to think of themselves as "taxpayers." Being a taxpayer implies a duty to pay "your fair share."

This mental process is not by accident. It is a mental condition of servitude created with intent and purpose.

Now there is a second huge reason for the income tax. The income tax system implies that legitimate taxes are owed by the people to the government. Also the income tax implies a legal and legitimate accounting system or a debit and credit system like all governments (except the Federal Government) must have.

That Federal income tax is needed to fund the Federal Government is a charade. The income tax system covers up the fact that the government pays for nothing. It gets everything for nothing.

But the system does not want you to know this. The system would collapse if it became general knowledge that paper money cost the government nothing but transfers wealth to the government for nothing.

It is an illusion to believe that human liberty is possible in or under a paper money system. Sorry!

We have said that income tax is not for income to the Federal Government. Income tax does have another big purpose and that is to control and regulate consumption.

A fascist regime always regulates consumption. To regulate consumption is to regulate the volume of paper money. Regulation of the volume of money regulates the perceived value of money.

If you have read a lot, you certainly have heard of John Maynard Keynes, the darling of the printing press socialists. Keynes revealed in his 1920 book, *Economic Consequences of the Peace,* the real secret of free printing press money. He stated that: "If governments should refrain from regulation (taxation), the worthlessness of the money becomes apparent and the fraud upon the people can be concealed no longer."

So the regulation system called the income tax conceals the worthlessness of the money. This is what Keynes is saying.

Why this takeoff on paper money? It is our belief that it is impossible to understand politics, government, and the reality of life and the accumulation of wealth without knowledge of how the money creators create money out of the air, yet you have to work for it.

All paper money depreciates over time, but since it is gradual, it is imperceptible to the people. They get raped and impoverished gradually.

People do not think and plan long term. To accumulate assets and plan any sort of realistic long-term security, we must understand paper money and gold. Gold is money that preserves wealth.

Just So You Will Know

The elite who rule America are mostly out of sight, but their philosophy and politics is well known to researchers.

There are two things that you should know about these "people." First, they are neither Democrats nor Republicans. They have no such thing as a political label. They finance and control all sides, the communists, the fascists, and the Nazis. To them, democracy is a joke and for entertainment of school children. If they have a religion, it is Luciferianism.

Second, they all believe in and promote paper money. They are the money creators. Their vast wealth has been devised from creating paper money. They transfer wealth from the people to themselves with paper money.

Since they absolutely control the volume of money, they control America. The more paper money they "spend," the wealthier they become. Their wars and revolutions are highly profitable.

Debt? Are you kidding? They are inflating away "debt."

What is debt? According to *Webster's Seventh New Collegiate Dictionary,* first copyrighted 1916: "Debt" is something owed, an obligation."

The U.S. national debt is a world-class scam simply because it doesn't exist. What an amazing deception!

Oh, yes, the so-called national debt is pretended as well as payment is pretended. This whole charade violates the plain meaning of the English language.

Why the scam? The answer is so simple. If there was no pretended debt even the crowd could see the worthlessness of the paper money.

Can't we see that this pretended debt instills confidence vitally needed to keep the scam going? Yes, confidence!

Spending? Everything you can read talks about how government spending is causing awesome debt. Again the *Webster* definition of Spend—"To use up or exhaust."

Therefore, these definitions do not apply to government finance. The government can not use up or exhaust its imaginary money that it can create to infinity. To instill confidence (the system is a confidence game), the money creators must promote propaganda that A.) the government spends large amounts of money. And B.) the government owes huge debt.

These negative concepts actually promote confidence because monetary activity of the Federal Government is framed in conventional accounting terms.

Fact: There can be no spending and there can be no debt when the source is infinite. Federal Government "accounting" is a myth.

When the government imposes its imaginary dollars on the American people, it does so with numbers. The numbers symbolize the imaginary dollars leading people to believe that they are real, that they have value, and are a store of wealth. These beliefs are called confidence.

What is the difference in a $5 Federal Reserve note and a $100 Federal Reserve note? The answer is the numbers. It costs the money creators virtually nothing to make a $5 piece of paper and no more to create a $100 dollar piece of paper.

These numbers are imaginary but they have perceived value. They must have perceived value or the confidence system wouldn't work.

It is the volume of numbers that reveals the scheme. The higher the volume, the less the perceived value of single numbers. It's called inflation.

Inflation is a hidden tax on the people. Few realize this. Inflation of the numbers (dollars) is a diabolical scheme to steal without guns and war. Typically governments use inflation against their own population.

But now the U.S. Government is exporting inflation to trading partners. Foreign countries are accepting imaginary dollars for hard goods that they manufacture.

Debt is real to you and me. Unlike the Federal Government, we have to give real value to get dollars. So do the States.

The U.S. Government corporation is the richest corporation in the world because they have a money-creating monopoly and police power to protect it. And they have the collective mind of the American people bought with paper money.

Finally, there is no real effort to stop inflation. The money creators want inflation as long as it's controlled. As long as they can manipulate public confidence they control the system.

Right now they are manipulating the numbers to keep public confidence. Inflation is an esoteric (hidden) system of transferring the wealth of the nation to them. Hence the political push to pass the Federal Reserve Act of December 1913.

The money creators know that their paper money is inflation. The people believe that inflation is increasing prices.

The government/bankers could care less about pretended deficits, balance of trade, and helping the American people preserve their assets with a sound currency. What they are really interested in is making sure that they keep the people deceived and confused about the truth of their mass theft with paper money.

Once they create the money, all they have to do is control the volume; i.e., the numbers. Come now, if you had a printing press to print paper money, would you be concerned about owing debt? Is this too simple for us to understand?

Summary: The government and its controlled media use conventional accounting terms such as "spending" and "debt" because these words hide the money fraud. "Spending" and "debt" are meaningless when money is created in infinite amounts.

But the words are important to the system because they imply that government finance is legitimate accounting. Even though these words are used negatively, they still have the same effect on the public mind. It works! Now every writer in the land harps on U.S. "spending," "debt," "trade deficit," etc.

Everybody is in shock and awe of "the U.S. debt." They are looking at a myth and think that they see the real world. The money creators are laughing.

Gross Deception

Why is there a place for private publications in America like *The Bob Livingston Letter?*

The answer is simple and straightforward: There are a growing number of people who no longer trust conventional wisdom.

Conventional wisdom is what most people believe. Conventional wisdom comes from the news media, public schools, the medical establishment, churches, and the government.

It's a lifetime programming process that builds parameters of thought from which few escape. And precious few do escape.

Conventional wisdom doesn't take on some people. By nature they question authority.

People progress away from conventional wisdom at various speeds and levels. Some people begin to doubt on an elementary level, while some completely reject any form of conventional wisdom.

There are two words that describe conventional wisdom and they are control and conformity. These terms are self-enforcing. That is, if there is control there is conformity. And if there is conformity, there is control.

Every government in history seeks conformity and control. They do this by and through the sources listed above which we shall call the system.

Psychological warfare is the system's chief weapon against its own citizens. The more perfect psychological warfare, the more perfect is control and conformity.

The system today is fine-tuned and it has great predictive value. The system that programs the public mind knows what the public thinks and can predict and measure any response to any probe.

We are the most conditioned, programmed beings the world has ever known. Not only are our thoughts and attitudes continually being shaped and molded, our very awareness of the whole design has been erased. Few question anything.

One important thought here: A person's I.Q. or education level has absolutely nothing to do with their perception of reality. Higher education is higher brainwashing.

Sometimes it seems that the more education, the bigger the fool. I myself went through four years of college, worked on a master's degree, and attended law school. What a pity! It took valuable time and money for me to pay for the brainwash.

It took years to get over it. I had to completely erase this education foolishness before I could begin to have half sense. My inquiring attitude and much, much reading helped me escape the programmed maze that entrapped me.

The many conflicts and confusion was emotionally and financially costly. The brainwash is so complete that only special people like you readers of this *Letter* ever get through the net. I mean this sincerely!

Why not just go through life asleep and enjoy the bliss? Well, you might enjoy your ignorance, but the price may be extremely high.

I am now in my 70s. I suspect that except for my special understanding of government motivation, I may have been killed in the Korean War. Later on I had a few chances to be foolishly exposed to surgery that could have done me in.

Neither my wife nor I have ever yielded to any doctor recommendations for surgery and many drugs. We just politely refused or trashed prescriptions for drugs.

Yes, my focus is on esoteric history, government, natural

health, and financial markets. My findings have stood my family and me quite well. I only wish that I could tap every one of you to join my success and my wonderful life derived from consistent and obsessive inquiry.

Well, anyway, you benefit from these *Letters* if you are getting the meaning and spirit of them. It is my firm belief that you will join my perspective to the extent that you do your own reading and inquiry. If you're too busy, you are too busy, or if you are too lazy—well, you are not lazy or you wouldn't be reading this *Letter.*

Now back to conventional wisdom: Conventional wisdom is what everybody believes. And what everybody believes is wrong, even if what they believe was believed by their ancestors.

People are obsessed with believing what they have always believed without question. An inquiring mind is required for anyone to question long-held views.

Now here are some examples of conventional wisdom. This is what most people believe:

- That government will not lie or allow an economic depression.
- That history as taught in schools or history books is truth.
- That pharmaceuticals sell good drugs that aid cures.
- That vaccinations bring immunity.
- That they can "catch" disease from someone else— germ theory.
- That the cure for cancer is just around the corner.
- When a child is sick he needs antibiotics.
- When a child has fever he needs Tylenol®.
- Hospitals are safe and clean.
- That drugs are not poison.
- That doctors and hospitals do not cause deaths.
- Guns are dangerous.
- World War I made the world safe for democracy.

- World War II was for democracy to prevail over tyranny.
- The Korean War was to contain communism.
- The Iraq War was to find and destroy weapons of mass destruction.
- Paper money is wealth.

There is a science and massive effort to create and manipulate public opinion in America. Do you remember the reason? It's for conformity and control.

The nature of governments is to perpetually grow, and the nature of politics and politicians is for wealth and aggrandizement. They represent government, not you.

Governments and politicians mask their agendas and create illusions to deceive and misrepresent. Governments, bureaucrats, and politicians look upon the public as a herd that should be deceived and led for the benefit of government and the elite.

Edward L. Bernays, the nephew of Sigmund Freud, is the father of manipulative propaganda in America. Mass persuasion and mass hypnosis is the fundamental of so-called democracy.

This is from Bernays' book, *Propaganda:* "Those who manipulate the unseen mechanism of society constitute an invisible government which is the true ruling power of our country. We are governed, our minds molded, our tastes formed, our ideas suggested largely by men we have never heard of. In almost every act of our lives, whether in the sphere of politics or business in our social conduct or our ethical thinking, we are dominated by the relatively small number of persons who understand the mental processes and social patterns of the masses. It is they who pull the wires that control the public mind."

Industry and commerce jumped on the spin to build their public images for bigger profits. Who do we think funds the front called the International Food Information Council to pacify the public on genetically modified foods? Right—Monsanto, Du Pont, Frito-Lay, Coca-Cola, Nutrasweet—those in a position to make fortunes from GM foods. Herr Goebbels admitted that he learned mass psychology manipulation from the Americans.

What is the lowest on the agenda of the massive brainwash? What has no commercial value? The answer is public health and personal liberty. The system is historically opposed to these.

No judge will rule on any issue of truth about public health or personal liberty. They have dumbed us down. We are on the animal farm. They rape us daily and we never question their criminal intentions.

Friendly Persuasion

The perfect slaves are those who can be persuaded to serve the state against their own best interest.

Long ago the social alchemists developed the art of propaganda. They discovered that persuasion as a system of enslavement is far superior to the rack and the thumbscrew.

Persuasion is far superior at creating obedience, docility, and an altered state of consciousness with no risk to the state. Furthermore, this mind-altering process is automatically passed from one generation to the other without cost to the state.

Public education as a dumbing down process is the ongoing basis of Orwell's *Animal Farm*. A programmed population will endure unbelievable financial and bureaucratic punishment and insult with the full cooperation of the victimized people.

Governments Can Stay in Power if...

1. They can continue to deceive most of the people.
2. They can very gradually reduce human liberty.
3. They have a method to steal the people's assets without hostile awareness over a long period of time with inflation and income tax.
4. The key to government power is gradualism. Anything can be accomplished over a long period of time. People accept their conditioning no matter what it is. I have found that the very first step toward awareness is to become suspect of all politicians.

Agents of Change

Battle for the mind: How they do it. Any religion that has group identity is by definition an organized religion. Religion prescribes parameters of thought and religion prescribes thought. There are few exceptions to this.

Governments desire organized or group identity religion because they can be manipulated without any awareness by the group. Religion is in general "tax exempt" because organized religion is pro-government and pro-authority. Any group has group thought and group expression.

All individuals become faceless and mindless. To the extent that one is a group member, to that extent that a person surrenders individual identity or ego.

The group's first step is authority. The more organizations that authority can get the people involved in the easier the control and manipulation, because all groups espouse altruism. Group identity can be any religious group, any fraternal group either secret or open, and any social group.

What about Christianity? Christianity is a personal and individual religion anathema to organized religious and regimented "spiritual" systems. The stronger the group's appeal, the more one can be led into and deceived by altruism and altruistic appeals.

Governments strive to move humanity from the ego or self to the group—the foundation of government deception and power.

They use:

1. Controlled media

2. "Public education"

3. Organized religion

4. Fraternal organization (both secret and open)

5. Many, many subgroups.

Charities and organizations impress upon one's psychic concepts pseudo "facts" that are not provable and have no foundation in fact, but are accepted as an absolute generation after generation.

The same is foolish to the individualist who by nature or who has a natural inclination to inquire into anything without inhibitions. As one loses his/her identity to group thought, then he/she becomes manipulated by phony altruistic pronouncements of politicians and authority.

This is to say when one loses self he is transferred to group thought. We are one or the other.

Altruism is morality based on the philosophical premise that man lives for the sake of others... that man's life and property are available for sacrifice to "higher causes, e.g., the common good the public interest, society, the needy, the world, God, country."

In practice, it's who will sacrifice whom. You guessed it. It's the non-producer political power transferring the wealth, production, and the public will to itself. They do this with great ease once they instill altruism in the public mind with the group concept.

Competent people who act on reality have gone underground in these latter days of political suppression. They are fully aware that hyper-individualism now, though not coded, is tantamount to crime against the state.

What about Warren Buffet and Bill Gates? They certainly understand capitalism and the accumulation of wealth, but they well know to bow their knee to Baal with their espousal of charities and social dispensations, as Bill Gates heavy involvement in vaccination in Africa.

Do they know that they are appeasing authority or are they mind-altered with altruism? Possession of ones' ego is to live in reality. The ego is the self and means individuality.

The common use of the word ego implies vanity, but our use here simply means the ultra-expression of the individual as opposed to the group. Group dynamics promote altruism and a mind locked out of reality. It's a long road back, and few arrive except those few who will read the right material without reservations or bias.

Groups socialize and dehumanize. Communication fails between husband and wife, between neighbors, between professional associates, etc., etc., in direct relation to group influences and their degree of altruism.

Authority abhors individuality. It is the destruction of the individual over time that has moved us to the fascist state. Think Nazi torchlight parades.

Herr Hitler used the morality of altruism with his "higher good" to which anything and everything should be sacrificed for the "National Will."

Psychological Warfare & Full Belly Starvation

We use the term "psychological warfare" because the battle for the mind is indeed the most malicious type of warfare.

We are programmed by the system. What's more, our programmed beliefs go from generation to generation the same as genetics. Unless we break the pattern of programmed thought we may hold erroneous beliefs for hundreds of years without question.

We build our lives or we self-destruct according to our ability and our inclination to break the programming code or preconditioning of the system. Not many do. The philosophy of the system (government) must be evaluated in terms of human liberty.

Human suppression is more psychological control than physical coercion. Those who control our minds control our physical and monetary assets including our physical bodies.

The art and science of mass mind control is now in its heyday. The fact that no one suspects it, attests to its perfection.

Totalitarianism by and of the elite has been refined into a "benevolency" that is embraced by the people. Indeed the people have been seduced to their enslavement through mind control. Evil has been made to appear good and good has become evil.

Psychological warfare excludes objective reality. There are no options to choose that would benefit the individual. All options are funneled toward the benefit of government and the elite. All that's left is myth and counter-myth, like the Republican and

Democrat candidates for President—no options for the people.

Psychological warfare extends no less to nutrition and health. Amazingly, malnutrition passes from generation to generation as certain as human genetics. A weakness that is developed in one generation passes to the next.

However, upon reintroduction of adequate nutrition within one or two generations, health can be reversed. It's called disturbed heredity by Dr. Weston Price.

Insensitivity is The Key

The essential purpose of group psychology is to desensitize the individual mind. It works like magic.

Witness the insensitivity of people today. They will literally accept anything. Believe me, the politicians and bureaucrats know this and use it for ongoing deception.

Manna to the group is poison to the individual. It is therefore the evolvement of the group or mass mind, which has brought us to our present state of insensitivity. Tyranny follows, and it is here!

The basis of the psychology of group dynamics is that people are naturally gregarious. They feel secure in groups and quickly become dependent on groups.

The group is a control mechanism that builds insensitivity. The more group oriented we become, the individual mind merges into the group and therefore becomes insensitive to reality and indeed hostile to reality. This is nothing short of psychological warfare and is the fundamental control system of authority.

All the thousands of organizations didn't just appear over the centuries. They were inspired for control reasons. Simple "brotherhood of man" sounds innocent enough, but it's awesome in empire building. The group or the herding instinct vastly lowers the need for aggressive police power.

The more the masses are herded, the fewer people needed at the top to control and run the show. The more people are herded, the easier they are propagandized and persuaded.

Finally the public mind merges with the government or authority. This is George Orwell's *Animal Farm* where the people are controlled with and through deception, but they are not aware of it. In fact, they love big brother. They love deception! This syndrome is what we have repeatedly referred to as benevolent totalitarianism.

Authority is absolute but the broad use of jackboots and the dreaded midnight knock at the door is no longer necessary. We do indeed have the same fascism as Nazi Germany, but it has been over the past 50 years skillfully honed and polished into an acceptable benevolence with the cover name democracy.

Hitler also used the powerful mind-altering word "democracy." He said that Nazi Germany was a great democracy.

We are truly on George Orwell's *Animal Farm* NOW! What's more, we love our masters and all their sadistic control system. We are now prepared for an advanced tyranny under the cover of the "Patriot Acts." Anybody not desensitized knows that the "Patriot Acts" are war on the American people and human liberty.

We are now face-to-face with a modern star chamber. Patriotism is the cover. The American flag is the symbol. The current "election process" is devious political demagoguery.

The whole purpose of the political charade is the further advance of altruism. What a scam and what deception.

Altruism Leads to Orwell's *Animal Farm*

Altruism is that which one least suspects. It has a double meaning.

To the unsuspecting public it appears good, but it is hypocrisy with a hidden agenda to cover evil. It is the philosophical basis of democracy and benevolent totalitarianism.

Webster's Dictionary, seventh edition, defines altruism as "regard for or devotion to the interest of others, unselfish, all heart, bleeding heart, charitable, generous, humanitarian, kind, magnanimous, philanthropic, self-sacrificing." This is as the public mind sees altruism. But what is the truth?

The truth is to gain power, control, and wealth under a veneer of good and charity. Unveiled, altruism is hypocrisy, deceit, egotism, love of money, criminal politics, "patriotism," nepotism among the elite nobility, brotherhood of secret societies, manipulation of the public mind, and its production.

Background: The organized church is a social organism that has over time translated Christian morality into social morality, creating the political foundation of "democracy" and altruistic government. When Christian morality becomes social morality (humanism), evil becomes good and good becomes evil in the public conscience.

This is esoterically called building of the temple which is now complete and the capstone of the all-seeing eye is in place. The temple is the temple of humanity as symbolized by the pyramid on the dollar bill.

The love of and for Christ has now become the love of humanity and human depravity. Planners designed and created altruism as the blueprint to funnel the people to the animal farm. The people must be controlled without being aware.

Non-awareness is the key. Dumbing the population down with public education and very sophisticated altruistic propaganda prepares the people for social leveling.

Altruism cleverly hides the depravity of human nature. It makes evil appear good and good appear evil. See no evil, hear no evil, do no evil permeates the propaganda. What's under the mask of altruism?

The answer is things that sound good but undermine society such as big business philanthropy. Excellent examples of this are Bill Gates' "gift" of billions for worldwide vaccinations of children, the nationwide promotion of commercial milk as a health food, wars to bring "democracy" to subjected people, public education to dumb down the people, widespread starvation because of commercial foods empty of nutrition, and general and complete destruction of public health with sugar, a drug industry that preys on the public under the pretense of medical cures. The list goes on and on.

The goal of altruism is to conceal the political agenda, promote ignorance of public health, create a state of mind of dependence on government and the medical establishment, and quash every form of individualism, independence, and creative thinking, promote ignorance of monetary realism whereby government can perpetually transfer wealth to itself with "money" that it creates and promotes organized religion to support the "morality" of government and the system.

Building The New World Order is the building of the new man with a neutered mind that does not know good from evil. When the human mind evolves to the point of not knowing good from evil, it has become evil.

Society becomes neither male nor female but one mass of sub-humanity united with the state. America is now Orwell's *Animal Farm*.

When men and women come to a state of conscience, not knowing good from evil, they are given over to a reprobate mind. Romans 1:28. Men love darkness because their deeds (and thoughts) are evil. John 3:19.

Blessings to you who understand.

CHAPTER 2

The Economy & Your Wealth

From its beginning, *The Bob Livingston Letter* has served to guide readers through the dangerous minefields of wealth accumulation, preservation, and protection. The task demands being constantly alert and quick to respond to the ever-present threats from predators, both public and private, always on the prowl to separate us from the wherewithal that is rightfully ours.

Bob Livingston's incisive and often prophetic insights on economic developments and investment strategies arm the reader to cope successfully in today's dangerous financial environment.

Some of the following articles prove that point, as Bob warned of collapse in the housing and stock markets long before they occurred.

The Pin Gets Closer To The Housing Balloon

(This appeared in The Bob Livingston Letter, Nov. 2003)

Right now the public mood is in a temporary state of hopeful recovery underpinned by an ongoing massive expansion of credit. In other words the continued expansion of credit and debt has re-ignited the stock mania and the public euphoria that always goes with it.

Underneath, the pin comes closer to the housing balloon. It's only a matter of time. At this point in time the housing bubble pop in the U.S. will have worldwide impact.

Rising long-term rates have already had a negative effect on housing refinancing. Therefore, the short bout of economic strength at this time will be followed by another vicious downturn.

I see the housing bubble about to deflate along with rising long-term interest rates. The housing mania in the U.S. and several other countries is so big that its collapse is a huge risk to the U.S. economy, the stock market, and in fact, the world financial system. That 75-year-old ingrained belief that land values and home values always go up will be shattered in the coming months.

People give little thought to the near-term possibility that they can quickly owe more than the market value of their homes. They do not realize that their homes will fall in value as mortgage rates directly deflate home prices by reducing affordability. The American people today have had no experience with devastating national housing deflation.

Adjustable mortgage rates is an explosion in the making. Adjustable mortgage rates were at the crux of the British housing crash of the early 1990s. But this was tiny compared to the brew now boiling.

Just think, this housing time bomb was created during the biggest boom in American history. No one would dare express concern that an unbelievable economic collapse would come out of such prosperity down the road.

Rising unemployment along with rising long-term interest rates will be the kiss of death to the real estate market. But please understand that Tokyo real estate has lost nearly 70 percent of its value over the last decade despite continued low interest rates. Worsening unemployment alone undercut the Japanese real estate market.

Realistically, it would be foolish for us to ignore that a great housing and land deflation is upon us. The commercial real estate and housing market is at very high risk to corporations, to individuals, and to the United States economy.

The U.S. market is too big not to be international in scope as foreign buyers are heavy into the U.S. secondary mortgage market. Certainly the historical record implies that the deflationary collapse will at least equal the mania.

And historical records always show, after the fact, the irrationality of the mania which very few can see while it is still in progress as now. This is not the time to buy a home or commercial real estate! It's time to sell and rent until the real estate crash comes and goes.

Several nations are extremely vulnerable to the housing price bubble. The real estate crash is dead ahead!

Subprime Loans

(This appeared in The Bob Livingston Letter, Aug. 2007)

The Center for Responsible Lending estimates that 2.2 million borrowers who got subprime loans since 1998 either have lost or will lose their homes through foreclosure over the next few years. This includes one of every five borrowers who got subprime loans in 2005-06, a default rate unmatched in the history of the modern mortgage market.

Prudent Projections

Thoughts for you to think about: In the progression of time the U.S. currency is depreciating toward zero. This is understood by the public as rising prices, but it is more specifically depreciating paper money.

Now I do not believe that the U.S. Government will collapse into chaos. I suspect they know what we know, that collapsing currency finally creates crisis in spite of statist propaganda. Therefore they must have contingency plans.

The government reacts to its interpretation of public perceptions, which are closely monitored. At some point a segment of the population will become aware of the worthlessness of paper money and trigger an alert to the greater population. This foretells monetary crisis and social chaos.

What will the government do? I would guess that the government will announce some sort of quasi gold standard which, at this point, will probably be fictional and it may or may not calm the people.

If it does not bring calm, further action will be announced. By this time there will be many new population controls and perhaps some negative propaganda directed at "hoarders" and gold owners etc. All is in preparation for this time of monetary crisis.

And guess what? At some point the government will have a serious need for gold and silver to back a new currency.

I don't think they will announce that gold (the metal) will be used currently as money. Instead a more likely event is to announce new currency with gold backing.

Silver money issued through 1964 will be used as emergency money. By that time we will probably be on a plastic money, since our current junk coins will have disappeared, according to Gresham's Law, which says bad money runs good money out of circulation.

Even now this event is rearing its head. Even junk money has metal in it worth more than the exchange value, i.e. the junk coins are worth more as metal than money.

The government will need gold. Then it may become known that there is no gold in Fort Knox. The government's options:

1. Confiscate gold in all bank deposit boxes and as much as they can get from individuals.
2. Nationalize all gold and silver mines.
3. Confiscate all Exchange Traded Funds (ETFs), gold, and silver. By that time this will be a huge bag of gold and silver and they are watching it. You don't think they will do it? Study history!

What are some options for you?

1. At some point in time (you to be the judge) begin to sell mining stocks and buy more gold and silver coins. How will we know? Watch the propaganda and new controls.
2. You should already have food storage and barter items as well as alternative power.
3. Educate those you care about as to the mechanics of survival. Not many will listen as long as they perceive no crisis.
4. You should have long ago been aware of the need for home defense. You fill in the blanks.
5. Obey all laws as far as possible.

What is it?

Everybody wants it the world over. We live and die for it. Our forefathers trusted it as we do. It is like a universal religion. It symbolizes wealth and prestige. It is a figment of the imagination—it is a fake, a phony, and a myth created by the silent rulers of the world. It's the biggest lie never told!

What is it? It's the U.S. dollar. And its modern alchemist is the United States Federal Reserve—a private money cartel. It creates wealth for some and steals wealth from the masses. Everybody feels good when they think about it and when they believe that they have it.

Politicians and government bureaucrats lie, cheat, and steal for it. World wars are fought and millions die for it. Men, women, and children jealously possess it. Millions deny themselves for it and millions hoard it. They believe in their hearts that it is the "real thing."

It is true love in the natural world but condemned in the spiritual world. It brings tribulation to men's souls. It was created in the minds of ancient alchemists to turn sand into gold. It has fooled wise men and fools alike for hundreds of years. It is a promise of nothing, a mental fiction.

Men trust it as a store of wealth and the passing of inheritances. Its secret has been revealed by esoteric sages, but it has such narcotic soothing that it blinds the mind and causes euphoric false confidence. It has the madness and insanity of love. It rules reason, doubt, and faith. It symbolizes comfort, material wealth, and security.

Modern tyrants only need to print money and call it democracy to rule the world and men's thoughts. Modern bankster dictionary: Deficits, budgets, national debt. All are euphemisms to camouflage the system as legitimate accounting.

The words are powerful and set in the national psychic. They are key words to hide the printing of money and the constant and ever growing transfer of wealth to the inner elite and their loyal supporters.

The widespread presumption is that the highly advertised Federal Reserve printing of money is to bail out a sinking economy. The truth is that the volume of money is in direct relation to the amount of theft of what's left of America.

It is total war against the American people. It is psychological economic warfare with the intent to cover the massive transfer of wealth. Modern money (dollars/credit) confiscates wealth!

Dollar diplomacy requires a triangle of power—the printing press, the military, and the IRS. What are the insiders doing with their phony money? They are exchanging it for gold, proving that their alchemy does work.

Real money, real wealth, and long-term value is gold. Who will be the last to find out and get cheated out? The people!

The Wisdom of General Douglas MacArthur

From the Ludwig von Mises Institute's website comes the insightful description of our current political environment: It is what General MacArthur wrote about the United States during the Korean War.

"Talk of imminent threat to our national security through the application of external force is pure nonsense... Indeed, it is a part of the general patterns of misguided policy that our country is now geared to an arms economy which was bred in an artificially induced psychosis of war hysteria and nurtured upon an incessant propaganda of fear. While such an economy may produce a sense of seeming prosperity for the moment, it rests on an illusionary foundation of complete unreliability and renders among our political leaders almost a greater fear of peace than is their fear of war."

Safe Deposit Box?

I realize that this is as American as apple pie but there is no such thing in the real world. U.S. banks are government institutions. There is all manner of precedent for seizing, blocking, breaking and entering "safe deposit boxes." Use at your own risk!

Client-Attorney Privilege in the U.S.?
Don't you believe it!

All U.S. attorneys are under the heel of the IRS and so are foreign attorneys who help U.S. citizens with tax problems.

Client—accountant privilege? No, not even pretended. Anything disclosed to your accountant is disclosed to the IRS and all government. This is the law! Attorneys and accountants work for the IRS but of course you pay them. No, there is no income tax law that makes you liable but there is IRS police power force de jure. Be realistic! Pay for the "privilege."

Gold

The politicians destroy capital and savings as fast as they can but they are big promoters of gold.

It is hard to concoct a more geopolitically friendly case for gold than the one that exists today. Politicians of both parties have passed the gold bug dream stimulus package—free paychecks for U.S. citizens.

The Democrats offer more stimulus checks and new taxes on capital along with higher excise taxes. The Republicans offer more war and military spending. Somewhere along the line all this fiat money will force rising interest rates.

Even though higher rates will be forced, the Fed will claim that it is "fighting inflation." Contrary to conventional wisdom, rising interest rates will be accompanied by a soaring gold price. The only threat to the gold price is when inflation adjusted interest rates turn positive.

I can't imagine how long this will be, but it will be a while. I still expect a very high gold price built upon the carcass of the U.S. dollar. They say that central banks (central manipulators) create money out of nothing. This is not really true.

They actually create "money" by reducing the value of every dollar in existence, foreign, and domestic.

Federal Reserve magic money is still a numbers game. The bigger the numbers of new money the less each unit is worth of the new and old money. There are still trillions of dollars in retirement and savings.

So many, in fact, that the inflation is slow enough that most people can't figure out what is happening. More will wake up if—and as—we move into hyperinflation, but still most people will not be able to sort out cause and effect. This age of currency depreciation is the impetus for mass manipulation of data in an attempt to hide the debauchery of the currency.

There is no question that the Consumer Price Index (CPI), the Gross Domestic Product (GDP), and jobs reports are flawed. Don't forget that most people believe the official numbers even though, in the case of the CPI, the government admits that food and energy are not included. Yet people still believe the numbers.

Though the precious metals have corrected and have been dormant for a while, a base is building that will finally push the metals into a speculative blow off at no telling what price.

But we still have the credit bust that has the capacity to turn nasty. People are pursuing safety by accepting negative real returns just to insulate their notional wealth. U.S. 10-year treasuries are now yielding roughly 4 percent even though broad measures of the money supply are growing at an estimated 16 percent rate. This is crass but it is happening.

The destruction of savings is unbelievable for Americans. As if this is not money negative enough, inflation is taking another big bite.

I can tell you that the middle class is on the way down and out. The only way to stop the hemorrhage is to exchange fiat paper for precious metals which will appreciate faster than paper money will depreciate.

So what if there is a real crash and deflation? Gold has in the past appreciated during depressions. During scary economic collapses even as the money supply contracts, people become afraid that the system and the currency will go. They buy gold.

Modern money now is more than M1, M2, and M3. The new non-traditional financial instruments such as mortgage-backed securities and Collateralized Debt Obligations (CDO) are the new "reserves."

Call it whatever, but it is all hot air. Silently the Fed is *de facto* nationalizing the banking system. Will it crash this time? It is scary with the credit bust still busting and the banking system still searching for a bottom.

If it is possible to float the system upon fiat, it will be done once again. But it will be taken out of the dollar assets of the American people. Remember that the bigger the numbers, the less each individual dollar will buy.

The Secret of Getting Rich

"Be greedy when others are fearful, and fearful when others are greedy." — Warren Buffett.

All Warren Buffett is saying is to go opposite to the crowd. When the public is in despair, buy. When the public is euphoric, sell.

Just now the public is a long way from euphoric about gold, oil, and uranium. Buy! In life in general, always think and act opposite the crowd. The crowd is always wrong! The consensus of the public is your clue to reverse.

The Non-Bank Bank Account

Bank accounts in the U.S. or internationally are high profile. Banks are quasi-government institutions. This means that banks do the will of the government. Your interest is secondary.

There is no such thing as a private bank account in the United States. All records are available to the government. Foreign bank accounts over $10,000 U.S. are reportable on 1040 tax returns.

Non-bank bank accounts are under the government radar, but most people don't know about them. Even these accounts will be unavailable when the U.S. puts on capital controls.

Capital controls will come as printing press money creates one monetary crisis after another. After governments suck the wealth out of an economy with massive expansion of money and credit, they then turn like vultures on the assets of the citizens.

They slap on exchange controls to stop the hemorrhage of money and investments from leaving the country. People who understand the paper money system see these things in advance and will take action.

The rest wonder what happened and won't care either. At any given time in history, and in any country, only a small percentage of the people are shocked by bureaucratic tyranny.

The people who become alert to the parasite nature of government are without exception producers and savers as they have the most to lose. Those who have accumulated wealth are actually enemies of the state whether they are aware of it or not.

In reality the people exist for the government, not as they believe that the government exists for the people. So-called democracy is nonsense to a rational mind. It's the favorite word of politicians and bureaucrats used to throw altruistic sand in the eyes of the people.

The very best way to preserve assets is to first take them out of U.S. dollars. Then get them out of reach of U.S. jurisdiction, which means out of the United States.

The exception here would of course be gold and silver in your physical possession; and take delivery of your stock certificates.

The first non-bank bank account can be a Swiss annuity. Even though a Swiss annuity is a Swiss bank account in all but name, it is defined as an insurance policy and as such it is not reportable under the law.

The idea at this time is to denominate your Swiss annuity in Swiss francs and get currency gains against the U.S. dollar. Your money is accessible at any time in U.S. dollars.

The second non-bank bank account is goldgrams from *www.goldmoney.com*. Goldgrams is digital gold money, an international currency that is accessible anywhere in the world through the internet. GoldMoney (goldgrams) can be traded among members for cash or gold equivalent or one can just use his goldgram account to accumulate gold outside of the United States.

GoldMoney is not a bank. It is physical gold that you own in London. They are expanding their storage locations so that in the near future one may have choices where his gold is stored.

At any rate, it is now outside of the United States.

Your account can be accessed from anywhere in the world through the Internet. At the moment, GoldMoney accepts four currencies: U.S. dollars, Canadian dollars, Euro, and British pound. More currencies will likely be added.

GoldMoney is domiciled in the British Channel Island, Jersey, a 700-year old sovereign country with its customers' gold stored in London. They use SSL for encrypting, the same as with any online bank. This is as secure as the internet can be.

The GoldMoney people have been very careful in establishing GoldMoney. They have done everything possible to not give any government any pretext for attacking the digital gold currency (DGC) they created. They hold three U.S. patents.

Get full information and disclosure at *www.goldmoney.com.*

Here are some things to think about:

(This ran in The Bob Livingston Letter, April, 2005)

1. Have some cash money on hand at least six months expenses. Why? In a monetary collapse or deflation there is a serious need for cash in your hands, not in the bank; dollars would be scarce!

2. Be thinking about the time when there will be exchange controls in the U.S. It will come. Everyone should have a passport and money somewhere out of the U.S. The Swiss annuity is our choice for a "foreign bank account." Well, it's not really a Swiss bank account. It's much better. Currency gains last year plus interest were 28 percent. The Swiss annuity is still legal and much lower profile than a foreign bank account. It is not reportable. There is nowhere to report a Swiss annuity on U.S. tax returns as it's an insurance policy. It most likely will also end for Americans for a time.

3. Eventually, we will be in a blow-off of gold, silver, and uranium market and of course all commodities. Protect your profits with market stops. This should protect if you don't sell soon enough. Millions of people stayed in the New York market too long and lost their money. When the up-trend

changes, get out—we will tell you when.

4. Are you self-sufficient like everybody was trying to do during Y2K? Yes, have a generator and storage supplies including food. Hope you never need it, but if you do—it's cheap insurance. I have for many years been in a survival mode just in case. Remember squirrels store nuts for winter.

5. Live and keep a low profile. The politics of envy can bring back words like speculators and hoarders to your chagrin. Politicians are like mad dogs when they are after assets.

6. One of the main things to watch is the U.S. dollar index. If and when the U.S. dollar drops below 80, it's look out below. The authorities need and want a much lower international dollar. But they have to juggle the dollar down slowly with a lot of propaganda under it. All the "insiders" make money no matter which way things go. Don't kid yourself; they are quietly buying gold privately. They know better than anybody that their paper is no good.

7. Out two to five years: I expect the New York market to have been tanked. At some point, the Dow will cross gold as it did in 1980. This means that gold will be very high and the New York stock market (not gold stocks) will be low. If the U.S. dollar still stands, we will sell our gold stocks and buy the New York market. It won't be a jubilee. It will be the blackest pessimism that you ever saw. Many will believe that it's the end of the world. Then we will buy great values and begin the long trip back up; but one thing at a time. Let's stay aboard the commodity train awhile yet. We study the markets day and night and we will warn you when to get out. I hope you have a growing cache of gold and silver coins and gold, silver, and uranium stocks. I know that some of you have not or have very little. What will you do with your paper money? Gold and silver is the only way to keep up with the money creators.

To Keep and Bear Arms?

Canada passed tough gun control legislation requiring national registration of all firearms and making it a crime to refuse. Agents can break and enter without search warrants on mere suspicion of gun possession. How far behind is the United States?

If you have guns put them away, but be sure to check them for moisture and rust at regular intervals. It's a good idea to get them out and clean them periodically.

Encouraging news is that in the United States, 26 states allow citizens to carry concealed weapons. Talk about a crime deterrent!

Millions of Americans are aware that the authorities and their politicians are focused on disarming the people individually and collectively. This could never happen except through consistent propaganda that disarmament is for "public safety" in a time of rising crime.

Citizens rely on the Second Amendment of the Bill of Rights "...The right of the people to keep and bear arms shall not be infringed." James Hazel, who writes under the name Cutting-Edge Activism, has written an article entitled, *Blowing Away The Second-Amendment Myth*. Mr. Hazel makes the case that it is an illusion to rely on the Second Amendment for your authority to defend your right to keep and bear arms. That has been twisted in favor of the Federal Government.

Instead, he says that the best Constitutional authority is the Ninth Amendment: "The enumeration in the Constitution of certain rights shall not be construed to deny or disparage others retained by the people."

James Hazel says: "The rights of individuals to acquire, possess, carry, and use firearms of their choice for the purposes of defending their persons, families, property, or communities are not enumerated in the Constitution. Those vital unenumerated rights are ours. We retain them..."

I personally think that to rely on the U.S. Constitution at all is an illusion. Only the will of individual Americans to defend themselves will guarantee their right to private arms.

The gun control problem is a mind control problem. The authorities know full well that they, with all their high tech weapons, cannot subdue a determined people with private arms. This is why they want your guns.

The man or woman who silently keeps arms and learns to effectively use them is the greatest force there is in defense of freedom.

Stealth

According to *Webster's Third International Dictionary,* "stealth" means, "something stolen, the act or action of proceeding secretly or imperceptibly." And according to *Black's Law Dictionary* 6th Edition, stealth means, "secret or the act of stealing when the victim is unaware of the theft. Any secret, sly, or clandestine act to avoid discovery and to gain entrance into or to remain within residence of another without permission." Case cited.

In my view, stealth needs further definition. Stealth should be categorized as being in existence where there is total unawareness by the victim(s).

Also, stealth should be characterized as being secretly operative over very long periods of time, so as to be sacrosanct and institutionalized. One example is the Federal Reserve and its companion, the IRS.

Time bestows legitimacy. This means that millions of people are born into the system and never question its legitimacy, legality, or morality. The more generations that pass the more entrenched the stealth. So again, time bestows legitimacy and suffocates inquiry.

The people who understand stealth can understand government and predict the future. This, my friends, is a very, very small number of people. It is my prayer that all readers of the *Bob Livingston Letter* will understand stealth no later than reading this *Letter.* If so, you will be translated from the frivolous to reality.

The work-a-day world consumes the crowd. They have so much noise in their lives that they have neither time nor imperative to understand monetary realism and the legalized and official theft that is undermining every vestige of their lives and their future.

The stealth system of "legal" theft has been in place in the U.S. since the establishment of the Federal Reserve System and the IRS in 1913. Neither is legal but neither can be investigated and reversed.

We are on a fiat paper money dollar system and all who earn dollars and save dollars have depreciating currency with depreciating assets. Also, they have depreciating currency (inflation of prices) that slowly reduces the value of their savings and their standard of living.

The middle class destruction is in full view to anyone who has the wisdom to look. The stealth system has a cover of very sophisticated propaganda. Trust in the system guarantees the propaganda cover. People who trust the system never inquire past the propaganda and that is by far the majority, but not you.

The system operates on the certainty that the crowd will believe the propaganda cover. If the crowd stopped believing the propaganda, the stealth system would collapse and human liberty would return.

Also, when the stealth collapses the vast army of parasites, like lawyers, doctors, accountants etc., would have to get honest work. Oh, they are not all bad, but by far most are.

How do we escape the system of stealth? Start believing just the opposite of all political, economic, and geopolitical pronouncements. This alone will catapult you into reality.

If the trauma is too severe, return to slavery. You will be welcomed to become a "taxpayer" again.

Key to understanding propaganda: Governments never allow individual or media attacks on the esoteric monetary system i.e. the Federal Reserve and the IRS. The stealth system knows the propaganda value of phony opposition. Feigned opposition as in political parties keeps the simple blinded and all debate is on spurious issues. Decoys are as important to the stealth system as they are to duck hunters.

Spurious debate is a constant diversion. It is noise. The most "educated," professional, and sophisticated thinkers are conditioned and limited unless and until they escape the stealth parameters of thought. Until we believe that reality is outside the box, we can do no better than frivolity, diversion, and self deception. We can never know "cause and effect."

When thou encounters an educated fool, escape as fast as possible lest you be tainted with nonsense. People who never question authority, custom, and tradition, are unthinking fools.

Gradualism

Gradualism can overwhelm the public mind. Almost anything can be changed over time. Perhaps one of the elite collectivists' most powerful tools in gaining control of the world is their patience. They know that such change, if its social structure is to remain hidden and unknown to the general public, requires extended periods of time to slowly and unknowingly seep into the social structure of society. Decades mean nothing to them.

Many of the elite families have worked on the plan for centuries. Their signature trademark was the belief in the "inevitability of gradualness" that their ideas would eventually permeate into both government and private institutions, and from there spread out into society in general.

This is the basic philosophy of the Fabian Society (Socialists). Tony Blair and Gordon Brown are Fabian Socialists.

One of the hidden keys of National Socialism, now called "democracy," is that the government wants and promotes opposition, BUT ONLY ON SPURIOUS ISSUES.

Have you ever heard the politicians of any party, or bureaucrats, debate openly the Federal Reserve and the paper money system which has been stealing the production and wealth of Americans for 100 years?

Yes, they talk about such nonsense as budgets and deficits and debt but all are meaningless in a paper money system. The money power (meaning the fiat money power) is the greatest power on earth. They control the world system. They are mightier than military power for it is they who fund the military.

The only reason that we have small country enclaves is because the elite have to have a place to store their wealth. If they didn't control the fiat paper money system there would be no wars to advance their world system. No modern wars have been funded with gold and silver. They are financed under the name of "legal tender."

Translated, legal tender is forced slavery from the cradle to the grave.

Patient Gradualism

Many times we have used the term "patient gradualism" but we suspect that few understand the term or even know about it.

Patient gradualism is actually the concept used to blueprint world rulership by the few over the many. I should add that this concept is also the basis of keeping a steady flow of the wealth of the world (yours and mine) into the coffers of the elite.

Since the few elite are vastly outnumbered, they have to rule by deceit and manipulation. They are propaganda masters and they can make the people believe any ridiculous or stupid thing that they can create in their inner sanctum.

For example, they have over time taught the American people that cow's milk is a basic food and tantamount to motherhood. Milk has achieved the status of divine food to the point that almost nobody questions it.

Dairy milk today is what bread and circus was to the Romans. It cannot be separated from life or a life-giving food.

So what have our lord and masters done? They have gradually manipulated milk into pure commercialism. It is in fact today a non-food and a seriously negative substance which by no definition can be called a food for human consumption.

Now I read that "they" are ready to breed cows that can produce only skimmed milk, spreadable butter and unsaturated fats. This is laughable were it not for the fact that the population will embrace it and consume it. The people have been conditioned over time and they do not know the difference between nature and commerce.

The rule is that the people are always manipulated against their best interest over time. This includes their very lives and their health.

What is the truth about fake milk and real raw milk straight from the cow? The way "they" completely convert healthy raw milk to a synthetic non-food is to cook the milk under the pretense of purity, cleanliness, and shelf life, changing it from a potent allergen (a substance that builds natural immunity to allergies) to the most common allergy (disagreeable sensitivity).

The good bacteria in raw milk is killed and destroyed as well as the all-important bone forming enzyme, alkaline phosphatase. This substance is still sold as milk but the only similarity to it and raw cow's milk is that it is white in color.

Oh yes, they leave the milk sugar, which without the whole milk, is a huge factor in the diabetic epidemic in America. The only possible thing worse is fructose corn syrup which is now used in almost every packaged food.

As we have told you, so-called fructose corn syrup is not a food. It is not corn and it is not syrup. It is a synthetic sweetener that by-passes the pancreas causing it to eventually shut down, leaving a nation of diabetics.

We are almost there and all the diabetic sales paraphernalia is a testimony to a growing financial industry. It is big commerce and big pharma and the public are unaware.

My next prediction for the "milk" industry is production of "milk" without cows, only a picture of cows.

What about patient gradualism? You just saw it in the pure adulteration of raw cow's milk over a 75-year period. They had to do it over time.

The total reversal of values takes a long time and in many instances several lifetimes. The concept of "patient gradualism," simply stated, is that conspiracy committed over time becomes acceptable and even embraceable.

In other words, we accept things wholesale that would have triggered a revolution in the many years past. The ruling elite— who control the government—and the politicians calculate their goals to take years, surviving even the originators and creators of the esoteric blueprint of the New World Order. Planning is created and set up to be carried out and completed over generations.

Meanwhile, we the people have short-term horizons. We do not think in terms of generations, hence we cannot recognize patient gradualism as a phenomenon of world order.

Comes now to mind the men who created the Federal Reserve

System in 1913. They have long since been dead but their fellow bankers, symbiotic invisible government "public policy" creators, have carried on with all the wealth flowing to the system from the production and savings of the people.

The Federal Reserve paper money debt system was needed by the invisible elite to create wars and buy politicians. They also "buy" the propaganda to drive the public mind in any direction desired.

Propaganda is absolutely essential to the advancement of the New World Order. Otherwise, Caesar would have no clothes.

Also, fine-tuned propaganda literally protects the elite from the masses. And finally, organized propaganda is used to dumb down the people, making them less able to think and rebel against the elite.

And oh yes, the "educated and professionals" are driven into blinding parameters that shuts out or inhibits inquiry beyond their "professional pursuit." They are subjected to the same propaganda aimed at the masses with the same effect.

Few escape, save those like you readers who have inquiring minds beyond establishment propaganda. Finally, when the system has advanced its goals beyond a point that would trigger revolt, they reveal quite clearly their system even in their own official publications. They actually incriminate themselves but they do this knowing that few people will read their revelations and even fewer care.

The system knows when they are past the point to cause backlash or rebellion. It is difficult to get people to rebel against a system that they are born into, no matter how oppressive it in fact is.

Aaron Russo in his brilliant movie creation showed clearly that the U.S. has moved from "Freedom to Fascism," but few people care because fascism is still sold to the people as democracy, a term that the masses still equate with human freedom.

You can see how the establishment protects itself even in the face of exposure. If the word democracy is actually translated in today's world, it means that we embrace fascism just because it is wrapped in political altruism.

There is no such thing as unmanipulated human freedom. In "patient gradualism" we are today looking at a United States that began over 200 years ago at the Constitutional Convention.

The groundwork for statism and fascism started there. The entrenched system reveals its core philosophy and its paper money mechanism for human enslavement, an enslavement that imagines that it is free.

I quote now from *Money in Colonial New England* printed by the Federal Reserve Bank of Boston in 1973, page 33, giving a monetary history debate in 1973. Note how current this is for today: "Many congressmen realized that paper money itself was nothing but a form of disguised taxation. Said one legislator, 'The natural unavoidable tax of depreciation is the most certain, expeditious, and equal tax that could be devised. Every possessor of (paper) money has paid a tax in proportion to the time he held it.'"

But for "patient gradualism" and the psychic acceptance over time, millions of Americans would despise and be horrified at the paper money system that is daily—and even while they sleep—stealing their production and savings. We accept any sort of slavery if it comes about through "patient gradualism" over a long period of time.

In closing, I want to call your attention to one important thing. The Internal Revenue System implies intimidation and force, backed by police power. But the greater evil, which taxes all the users of paper money, is totally accepted, totally invisible, and without the enforcement of police power.

Everyone desires paper money accepted through "patient gradualism."

CHAPTER 3

The Stock Market

Seller's Remorse

"Well, I can't get out of the market now. I would lose too much money."

What does this statement really say? It says, "I can't take a real loss as easily as I can take a paper loss. A paper loss I don't have to face." It also says the government, the politicians, and the Fed won't let the market crash into a depression.

There is such a thing as seller's remorse. What most investors cannot endure is the realization that they have paper losses that will become real losses if they sell.

So they do nothing and sit on greater and greater losses rather than choosing to sell and redeploy what they have left. They choose to avoid regret at all costs. So rather than parting with a lemon and putting their money to work, they hang on to the bad investment, gambling that it won't go down further or that it will come back.

People are much more sensitive to negative than to positive stimuli. They feel that the hurt of losses won't be nearly as bad as long as they don't sell. This is a mind trap that millions have fallen into.

What actually happens in every bear market? Most people hold their stocks until they are worth only a few cents on the dollar. Then, when black pessimism sets in, they do what the crowd always does. They dump their stocks, swearing to never buy stocks again. Yes, they all sell out at the bottom just exactly when they should be buying. They will eventually buy again, right at the very top of the next bull market.

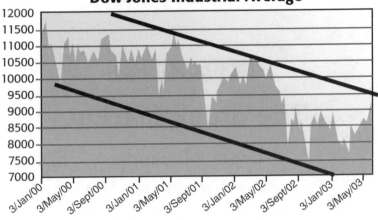

Dow Jones Industrial Average

Deceiving "Slope of Hope"

The crowd is riding that slope of hope to the bloody end. They always have.

The Cost of Denial

The public seems to be numb to cycles or bull and bear markets. They naively believe that once the stock market goes up for an extended period that it will continue.

Otherwise sober people tend to believe that the stock market is forever up, especially at the top. This sentiment of euphoria is slow to break and this is exactly why huge losses accrue before the public becomes shocked.

Charles H. Dow, founder and first editor of *The Wall Street Journal,* made the following observation in an editorial written in 1903: "There is always a disposition in people's minds to think that existing conditions will be permanent. When the market is down, it is hard to make people believe that this is the prelude to a period of activity and advance. When prices are up and the country is prosperous, it is always said that while preceding booms have not lasted, there are circumstances connected with this one which make it unlike its predecessors and give assurance of permanency. The one fact pertaining to all conditions is that they will change."

CHAPTER 4

The Deficit and the Dollar

"For this cause God shall send them strong delusion that they should believe a lie." 2 Thes 2:11

I have studied people for many years. Most simply follow the crowd and the crowd follows the propaganda.

The propaganda of the system provides blinders which effectively shut out all inquiry outside of conventional thinking. When non-conventional suggestions meet a conventional mindset, mental receptors shut down. There is total rejection and many times hostility.

We are in a vast concentration mind control camp developed through and by years of external stimuli of "public" influence. We cannot think or inquire outside of our invisibly prescribed parameters—some say, "outside the box." Unless and until we question "conventional wisdom," we never receive or process any doubt about the politically prescribed order of things.

All politics go into the same funnel when labels are removed. Political jargon becomes noise. Then the axiom of geometry applies to the masquerade of politics to wit: "Things that are equal to the same thing are equal to each other."

This is incredibly easy to see once the political party labels are removed. But this is a difficult or impossible task for the crowd. They love deception and delusion.

Politics and propaganda tickle their ears and so it will always be as it always has been. For any political system to function as created, there is and has to be vast deception. This statement is an entree into original thought. Many of you will have to stop right here.

But most longtime readers of this *Letter* will go on. I certainly don't want to pour new wine into old bottles. *"Neither do men put new wine into old bottles..."* Matt 9:17, Mark 2:22.

I speak now of my ongoing challenge to you that there is no "national debt" or "federal debt." This writing does not refer to state, county, municipal or private debt; only to the 100-year-old myth that we all believe, called the "national debt."

Only those who can't print money have debt. Why rehash this now? The answer is pure and simple. The false concept of "the national or federal debt," though negative, sustains a connotation of legitimacy wherein numbers, no matter how astronomical, preclude inquiry that they may be, and in fact are, meaningless.

Folks, this is a cover for political and monetary chicanery on a scale beyond the imagination of the mundane mind. The smartest people and the most "educated" accept this myth *prima facie* (on its face) with no thought of inquiry or challenge. There are few in America and indeed the world who understand monetary realism which is a study of substance vs. non-substance as money.

The American monetary system or non-system is fiat. Fiat according to *Webster,* "is the edict or decree of government authority. As it applies to fiat money, it is paper currency not convertible into coin or specie of equivalent exchange value."

Therefore real money is substance of intrinsic value. It is finite and limited by labor, production, and available natural metallic resources. It is silver, gold, platinum, etc., which is the only store of wealth as money, whereas fiat is a non-substance number system.

It is not the green paper but the numbers on the paper. It can be created to infinity and manipulated at will. Does it work? Yes, it has worked for 100 years. Why? Because it is a system of confidence and the depreciation of its exchange value is gradual.

People cannot focus on gradualism. Modern money is a thought system which is controlled by the controlling of the peoples' expectations and the manipulation of the volume of numbers. Where are these numbers? They are in your pocket on green pieces of paper which we falsely believe are dollars.

Peoples' expectations are manipulated by the manipulation of numbers. For example the official manipulation of the inflation numbers says inflation is less than 5 percent. John Williams in his *Shadow Statistics* site says and proves that inflation is 12+ percent *(www.shadowstats.com)*.

There can be only one reason for this huge difference in the numbers. Somebody doesn't want us to know how much and how fast our dollar assets are melting.

Controlling the numbers controls expectations and therefore extends the system, or non-system. Look at the green paper in your pocket which you think of as money. What is the difference between a $1 bill and a $100 bill?

The difference is in the numbers, not in the paper. What these green coupons really are is transfer coupons. Yes, they transfer our purchasing power to the money creators.

Every dollar printed dilutes all the dollars in circulation. Are we getting the picture?

Americans believe that they have trillions of dollars in savings and retirement. But what they really have is only numbers. Modern money is only numbers. It is not substance; it is fiat which is "money" by decree of "authority."

Modern day coin clipping is still going on, but in a silent deceptive way. It is much easier now. The production of new money is modern coin clipping. In other words, dilution of the money numbers is "coin clipping."

All holders of dollars get clipped. It is out of sight and gradual and the operation is so big that no one can see it or understand it.

What to do? The same as for years past: Buy gold and silver coins and keep them in your possession. Gold and silver have been better than all investments.

In the last month there has occurred a general shortage of 1 oz. American Eagle gold coins. There are dealers everywhere. Find one you can trust!

Also, Americans are stepping up their buying of Swiss annuities, an excellent and legal Swiss franc investment.

The Fed's Money-Making Machine

What does government creation of money really mean? Well, under disguise of economic crisis, the Fed is stealing the country.

Printing money is a crime if you do it. But if monopoly power of government does it, it's called "monetization." The government is now trying desperately to inflate because the more inflation, the more wealth is stolen.

■ Governments steal as much as they can without collapsing the system.

■ The more money they create for nothing, the richer and more powerful they get.

■ The bigger the government gets and the more reckless it gets, the more it must suppress its people because many begin to wake up.

■ The bigger government crime, the greater the propaganda and deception.

■ Fact: Every dollar the government creates means that dollar is stolen from the people. Paper money confiscates wealth.

Government deficit is a most deceptive term. The popular illusion is that the government is spending too much money. What is really happening? Everyone talks or writes about the government printing money, but what is really happening?

The act of money creation means that more and more of the national wealth flows to the Federal Government. How in the name of Pete do people think that the United States government became so powerful and so wealthy in property?

The government produces nothing. It has to steal, and it does so on an unimaginable scale. The mind of man cannot deal with such a massive transfer of wealth, and few people even suspect it. Why do people not know about the biggest fraud in history?

The answer is that the income tax serves to cover or mask the fraud perfectly. The minds who created this chicanery were masters of deceit. Is this crime too big to believe or too big to understand?

The government hides the fraud by getting the people to believe that the income tax supports the government and pays its expenses. The truth is that the government gets its wealth and power for nothing. It only has to create its money and the deception to hide what it is doing.

Writers, in trying to explain the U.S. trade deficit, lament that, "The U.S. has been living beyond its means." This serves as a mask for the truth that the U.S. Government has consumed the national wealth via the printing press.

Is the truth too horrible to face? How can there be such a thing as human liberty when the politicians and federal judges are paid and pensioned by the Federal Government?

We simply don't think.

The Coming Greenback Collapse

My prediction: The U.S. dollar will collapse as a direct result of an avalanche of printing press money. The dollar could go down to $.70 on the currency exchange and then, to restore confidence, there will be some form of a gold-backed dollar. It will have to happen somewhere in the future.

Most Americans do not as yet realize that this crisis is different. Our mountain of debt, negative personal savings, and huge trade balance deficit combine to threaten financial collapse. All the Federal Reserve can do is extend the imbalances and prolong the market crash. The only solution that the United States and world governments have is to print paper money.

What a paradox! Greenspan's paper money caused the mania in the first place and the subsequent collapse that we are now in. The only possible solution governments have is to destroy more wealth by collapsing the currency and the remaining wealth with more inflation. Thanks to the central bankers and their politicians, we now face economic collapse and inflation at the same time.

The list of problem bubbles is long: A consumer debt bubble, a dollar bubble, a bond bubble, a trade deficit bubble, the boomer retirement bubble, and the housing bubble. The basis of all the bubbles is debt that is collapsing. The collapse of debt is the essential ingredient of economic panics and crashes.

The big threat to the U.S. dollar is the huge trade deficit and the massive overhang of credit outside of the banking system.

Foreigners are still financing the huge U.S. current account deficit (trade balance) to the tune of $1.7 billion a day. They own 38 percent of the U.S. Treasury market, 20 percent of the U.S. corporate bond market, and 8 percent of the U.S. equity market. All this is a threat over the U.S. dollar and as the stock market crashes and foreign money flows dry up, the U.S. dollar will crash and by much more than expected.

For how much longer will foreign investors, who are financing the U.S. trade and current account deficit, be willing buyers and holders of American stocks, bonds, and the dollar? There certainly will be a time in our near future when the funny money fiat system practiced by the U.S. Federal Reserve Board will no longer hold confidence, leading to a sharp depreciation of the U.S. dollar.

When a national currency is destroyed and the economy collapses, the only recourse is gold. The point is, gold will have to be at a much higher price to back the U.S. dollar.

Those who hold gold will greatly benefit.

If you have gold buy more while it's cheap. *If you don't have any gold, start buying now.* You can buy American Gold Eagles from 1/10 ounce size up to one ounce. Buy a mixture. Gold is forever! Paper money is always destroyed by its greedy creators.

The major trend now is switching from financial assets to tangible assets.

Americans Put Lipstick On a Pig and Call it a Lady

Federal Budget is deciphered as meaningless. When will pieces of paper stop being accepted for food, service, and substance?

Modern money came from nothing and is going to nothing. This will be the flashpoint for gold like the crowd yelling "fire!" Financial speculation and widespread growth of gambling casinos always rise along with a speedup in the money-printing presses. Monetary and physical manipulation rise exponentially as the volume of printing-press money and credit rise.

Why gold? I will admit that I like the wealth effect of rising gold prices, but gold has other and more important attributes. It is shallow thinking to hear someone say that gold is a bad investment because it pays no interest. This implies a total misunderstanding of gold, to say nothing of the fiat paper money system.

Paper profits or interest received are good for a warm and fuzzy feeling. But the more serious reason for holding gold is for insurance against a total collapse of the financial system of fiat which eventually takes down all paper currencies. This will come.

If there is a key to investing and the preservation of wealth, it is wide diversification of assets. The current crisis should drive this home for all time.

My wife reminded me that she only feels secure with silver, gold, and Swiss annuities as almost everything was crashing. The spurt in the dollar is only temporary. It is a quirk that will reverse.

Although silver and gold went down in price, relative to everything else they held up wonderfully. Long-term holders of blue chip gold stocks should not be apprehensive.

The reason is that Washington will continue to destroy the U.S. dollar in their "bailout" of the U.S. and the world. Gold in hand and in the ground will be the only thing of substance left after the paper money empire collapses.

It is very easy for most people to get confused about long-term value (gold) versus the paper mania that just collapsed. All paper money empires throughout history breed excessive greed and overconfidence until all caution is thrown to the wind.

Before the collapse it seemed that everybody had a manic mentality. This state of mind promotes widespread gambling and the false euphoria causes a lapse in a sense of history of how the human condition always reverts to the mean.

Only a few people can see the need to turn some of their paper money (non-substance) into gold (substance.) Such "foolishness" never enters the popular mind, drugged on fiat.

Sober people always avoid the Ponzi mentality, no matter what the crowd is doing or the circus atmosphere. Is the government insane to drop cash (paper money) from helicopters? The people really are confused about what the government is doing.

There is much "opposition" to government policy. There are thousands of critics of government. *Bloomberg TV* interviews one critic right after the other.

Yes, the government (the corporate State) promotes its own opposition. BUT ALL OPPOSITION TO THE SYSTEM IS ALWAYS, WITHOUT EXCEPTION, ON SPURIOUS ISSUES. The public media is controlled and all "opposition" to the system is controlled. Opposition on or of fictitious issues promotes the government system.

Bush and company did away with *habeas corpus* in case real opposition arises. What is the veil? What is the mystery? The answer is that we are trying to put lipstick on the pig.

We are still trying to understand America in terms of capitalism and free enterprise, when in fact America is now a socialist country with a pretty face called democracy. But being in denial is to be perpetually deceived.

Listen, my friends: All fiat systems in history have been Socialist states, no matter the national pretense, as in democracy. All socialist states in history have a history of suppressing their own people. And all socialist fiat money states/countries transfer wealth and production to the state without payment.

Of course, as in America today, this transfer takes place via the depreciation of paper money. The owner of the money printing press owns and controls all wealth and production.

President James A. Garfield said: "Whoever controls the volume of money in any country is absolute master of all industry and commerce." This is not *Bloomberg News*. It is the quiet understanding of reality among those who want the truth, no matter what it is.

Socialism has great appeal because it promises the masses something for nothing. Say, isn't this the definition of fiat? Fiat is a social drug and it is terminal!

The coming hyperinflation that we envision is a product of fiat socialism. It is not, or will not be a failure of the free market or capitalism.

The gold standard is to capitalism and free enterprise what fiat paper money is to socialism.

Sovereign debt default is not some kind of sudden upheaval but gradual depreciation of the paper currency over time. In the U.S. the announcement by President Nixon of the closing of gold redemption by foreign countries in 1971 was the official declaration of U.S. sovereign debt default. It is then that the collapse of the U.S. dollar began, unnoticed by the American people.

It was at this time that the American people became drugged on fiat and skyrocketing personal debt. It was the beginning of the end of long-term bonds and other long-term contracts like life insurance. Currency depreciation robs retirement pensions and all savings, but most people don't notice because it is gradual up to the latter stages when it is already too late. Only those very few people who began to exchange their paper money for gold are able to preserve their wealth.

The government has an ongoing unofficial policy of suppressing the gold price simply because the authorities don't want the people's attention drawn to the depreciating currency. We are now in the latter stages where official statistics are manipulated in order to control the general perception of reality.

The rising crescendo of gambling casinos is proof that, although our official statistics are manipulated in favor of depreciating currency, the general population senses the depreciation and uncertainty of the paper money regime. Uncertainty and insecurity are the attributes of depreciating currency. It is a "quicksand" syndrome that arises like a drug addiction in the population.

Again, only a few put cause and effect together and silently take constructive action to accumulate hard assets. And yes, the prudent and the wise even store food against calamity and revolution.

Think with me now about the times we live in. Mattell® makes toy cars and Mattell® is now worth more than General Motors®, as someone has said.

Switzerland and the Swiss Franc for Protection vs. the Falling U.S. Dollar

Diversify and protect your assets!

Under Swiss law your Swiss annuity is outside the jurisdiction of a U.S. judge. Your funds are protected from U.S. bankruptcy or lawsuit.

Not a single Swiss insurance company has ever failed or gone bankrupt. The Swiss Federal Office of Insurance requires each company to maintain a security fund for policyholders that is segregated from the company's assets.

Your money is available at any time without surrender charges. Call 1-800-331-0996, and leave your name, address, and phone number to get Swiss annuity information.

Noise!

Few people realize how much noise there is in our daily lives. They don't know what noise is. Noise is a distraction, sight or sound that keeps us from thinking and focusing.

We used to put side blinders on our mule while plowing to keep the mule focused on staying in the furrow and listening to commands. We would tie a mesh sack around his nose to keep him from nipping the new corn.

Noise is extremely important in people control. People don't know the difference between noise and focus. Noise keeps us from being focused. The more noise in our lives, the less we are focused on reality.

Most advertising is noise to promote sales based on false needs. The most noise in our society comes from politicians and bureaucrats. These people can only stay in power if we don't think and don't stay focused on fact over fiction. We must decide what is important in our lives and establish priorities and avoid any distractions or noise. This is the direct route to wealth and happiness.

Now I will tell you what my focus is and what I think should be every American's focus.

Our daily focus is how to preserve health and preserve wealth. Most Americans are totally unaware of these two.

How to preserve health? The first rule is to be aware and willing to study and pursue alternatives. My thinking goes beyond this. I use orthodox or conventional medicine when I consider it necessary. But I believe that conventional medicine is absolutely controlled by the pharmaceutical cartel that also controls all allopathic doctors. Doctors lose their license to practice if they don't conform.

Moreover allopathic medicine is sickness, not wellness. Since it is profit motivated, this system has to have sick people to make a profit. It has no interest in preventive medicine. Immunizations are not a preventive or wellness system.

How to preserve wealth? Most people do not know and the system does not reveal that unfunded (unbacked) paper money has the purpose of transferring wealth from the people to the state (those who create paper money). This is hush-hush, and no politician or bureaucrat will discuss it.

The only exception that I am aware of is Congressman Ron Paul of Texas, and he is not a politician. He is a statesman and I pray that he stays alive and healthy.

Why does the paper money system work? It works because people don't understand it and because it is a system of gradualism.

Power over the people can succeed if it is gradual. Absolute tyranny can totally replace human liberty if it is a process of gradualism. It is sometimes described as two steps forward and one step backward. Time, however, works for the power brokers.

The few who preserve their wealth and prosper understand paper money. They accumulate assets such as silver, gold, and other precious metals. They also buy rare paintings, jewelry, and land. Paid for raw land in a safe country, I would consider a hedge against printing-press money.

And in today's world, keep aware of ways to transfer wealth to other countries while it is still legal to do so.

We have long recommended the Swiss franc and the Swiss annuity. You can call toll-free internationally at 1-800-331-0996 for more information. Let's reduce the noise to focus on health and preservation of wealth!

CHAPTER 5

Gold

Gold Glitters as Paper System Collapses!

Gresham's Law says that, "Bad money drives out good money." This is to say that paper money and credit created by governments drive out intrinsic value as gold and silver.

But what happens when the government money fails? People do as they have for thousands of years; they return to value and barter. Barter is the exchange of values not the pawning of credit.

Government money always fails. Real money always prevails. But the crowd has become addicted to paper and credit as money. They don't know that their paper "assets" are disappearing before their eyes as government printing presses dilute the currency with literally tons of "new money."

The idea of gold and silver as money has vanished down the memory hole. This generation has not the slightest understanding of real money. They could care less.

But the time has come and is now, that understanding real money as gold and silver may very well mean the difference in your survival and economic tragedy. For a time paper dollars will appreciate as we have a credit collapse, as now already in Japan. Paper money will actually be rationed, as it was in Argentina.

What will government do to respond to the crisis? They are 100 percent predictable. They will print more money, the very same thing they have done to create the collapse.

Then what will happen? Gresham's Law will be reversed. Good money will drive out worthless money. Yes, at that time the people, each man, woman, and child, will re-learn gold and silver as money. But it will take a lot of paper money to buy gold or silver—a whole lot more than now.

A collapse of currencies skyrockets the dollar price of gold. It always has. Government money is not value, and it is not a store of wealth. It is, in truth, a confidence game that confiscates wealth and labor and impoverishes the people over time.

Right now you are in a period of disappearing financial assets and entering a period of physical assets. Those who are aware will take action or have taken action to avoid the collapse of financial (paper credit) assets replacing them with physical assets.

It is time to be alert to the signs of a currency crisis and a credit crunch that could tie up your bank account and bring about a moratorium on your life insurance and annuity cash values.

Expect much tighter currency controls where the government monitors every penny you seek to transfer across borders. Yes, the money spigots can be wide open and still have a serious and prolonged credit collapse simply because the overloaded debt system is collapsing faster than the printing presses can print paper money.

Governments do not like for you to know that real money as gold and silver is an asset that you should own. Gold exposes paper money as a grandiose scheme to steal the world. The welfare state is by nature and by definition a paper economy designed to transfer wealth to the government free without the people being aware.

It works for a time, but greed and political chicanery cause the system to self-destruct. Sadly, the people's paper savings go with it. More and more financial assets need to be transferred to physical assets and the Swiss currency before the crisis becomes acute. We are in a crisis now but it's not yet visible to the people. It should be if they are reading about Argentina and Japan.

Government paper, i.e., T-bills and T-notes will be safer a little longer but finally the government may default on its debt as the system blows. Governments have historically repudiated their own debt when their money credit system collapses.

The public social mood has been slowly going down from the peak stock market mania in the year 2000. It is very obvious that financial speculation is collapsing. As we have cautioned many times, financial markets do not go straight up or straight down. There are corrections against the trend as the economic tides ebb and flow. The public never sees the trend until it is obvious and too late.

Everything that the Federal Reserve is doing is a futile effort to hold up financial speculation. They are guaranteeing a far greater collapse while they unwittingly are building a "foundation" for gold.

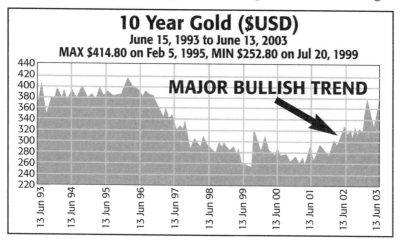

Two things are quite clear now. Gold sentiment is becoming substantially positive. Number two, bullion dealers and forward gold mine sellers are losing control of their derivatives suppression of the gold price. Their long manipulation of the gold price will create a violent and explosive gold price rise at some point. Gold price manipulation and gold miners hedging contracts amounts to a huge short of the tiny gold market which in the long run acts as a coiled spring under the gold price.

Unbelievably, the market cap of the entire gold mining industry approximates McDonald's® market cap. This should tell us something about the potential price of gold once financial speculation has completely collapsed along with false confidence in the U.S. dollar.

Silently, many gold stocks have already doubled. But be assured that the price of gold stocks and the gold metal have long and explosive price rises ahead. We are only in the beginning. Be alert! There is and there will be much political propaganda against gold and gold stocks. Officially, everything imaginable will be done to suppress gold and gold mining stocks. This is your cue to buy or to buy more!

Return to the Gold War

"You have a choice between the natural stability of gold and the honesty and intelligence of the members of government. And with all due respect for those gentlemen, I advise you, as long as the capitalist system lasts, vote for gold...

"...The moment we want to believe something, we suddenly see all the arguments for it, and become blind to the arguments against it." Quote by: *George Bernard Shaw socialist Nobel Prize winning author.*

"In the absence of the gold standard, there is no way to protect savings from confiscation through inflation. This is the shabby secret of the welfare statists' tirades against gold. Deficit spending is simply a scheme for the confiscation of wealth. Gold stands in the way of this insidious process. It stands as a protector of property rights. If one grasps this, one has no difficulty in understanding the statists' antagonism toward the gold standard." Quote by: *Alan Greenspan, former Chairman of the Board of Governors of the U.S. Federal Reserve.*

As we all know, Mr. Greenspan sold out to the money creators. He is the greatest inflationist of all time.

Untraceable Asset

Your reasons for buying gold remain the same regardless of the dollar price. Gold is private money. It is barter and has been for centuries. Gold held in your possession is an asset out of reach of bureaucrats who are seizing everything and anything under any pretext.

Gold is not a traceable asset if you first acquire it privately. This may not be always possible. Barter is outside the system, whereas the new currency, which contains metal threads and magnetic ink, means that large amounts of cash cannot get past borders and can be tracked inside the U.S.

According to W. G. Hill in the book, *Banking in Silence,* "It has been reported that at least some banks in the U.S. are already equipped with machines capable of reading encoded bills. U.S. currency is now completely traceable. The polyester thread that runs along the left-hand side of new bills is generally known by the public. What they don't know is that the polyester thread is or can be interwoven with magnetic threads, which can be encoded with your Social Security number at your friendly bank by just running your cash through their special encoding machines. This marks the bills and every transaction is easily traceable. Think about this nightmare."

The Real Alan Greenspan Reveals the Government's "Secret"

Listen to what Alan Greenspan said back in 1962 (when he was still Alan "Goldspan") — before he was on the government payroll: "The abandonment of the gold standard made it possible... to use the banking system as a means to an unlimited expansion of credit. They have created paper reserves in the form of government bonds which—through a complex series of steps—the banks accept in place of tangible assets and treat as if they were an actual deposit... The holder of a government bond or of a bank deposit created by paper reserves believes that he has a valid claim on a real asset. But the fact is that there are now more claims outstanding than real assets.

"The law of supply and demand is not to be conned... In the absence of the gold standard, there is no way to protect savings from confiscation through inflation. There is no safe store of value. If there were, the government would have to make its holding illegal, as was done in the case of gold... The financial policy of the welfare state requires that there be no way for the owners of wealth to protect themselves.

"This is the shabby secret of the welfare statists' tirades against gold. Deficit spending is simply a scheme for the 'hidden' confiscation of wealth..."

Fortunately, Mr. Greenspan is wrong about one thing. There are ways to protect and even multiply your wealth. They're just not conventional. And they definitely won't be available as the panic sets in and people really need them.

Debt is Meaningless If it is Inflated Away!

Government(s) presume to owe debt but they never intend to pay. They know that they will simply just inflate debt away.

All the politicians and everybody in government knows this fact but none will discuss it except Rep. Ron Paul. The American people know nothing about this swindle. If told, it is too incredible for most to understand or believe.

The concept of inflation or depreciation of the currency is the only basis for understanding government and the social order. Everything else is a diversion or frivolous.

In the U.S. the destruction of the currency has been going on since 1913. Until 1971 it was gradual. Since 1971, when Richard Nixon closed the gold window, inflation has visibly speeded up.

Now we are in the final stages when finally almost everybody can see that rising prices equals depreciation of the currency. In the current stage there is manipulation of public perceptions to divert attention from crisis and government-caused chaos. The dollar price of gold is suppressed and monetary indicators are fabricated.

All things that affect public understanding of reality are twisted and distorted in a massive attempt to cover open fraud and political chicanery. The political handlers of the decaying system are trying to extend the system as long as they can. They will not succeed.

It all but collapsed in August of 2007. The rot underneath is simmering and could erupt at any time. No matter how much new money or credit is created, it will only masque the final state of decay. It will only speed and expand the final collapse.

Put not your trust in any politician. Ron Paul is not a politician. He is a statesman!

Review often our survival list and concern yourself with personal survival. This is not an unhappy time if you know and understand monetary history and the vulgar political order. It is a time to give thanks that God has alerted us, blessed us, and has given us a chance to warn others.

CHAPTER 6

Wealth Preservation
Strategies for Financial Survival

Good judgment does not always accompany a good education or impressive professional experience. Where we Americans go badly wrong is trusting authority under the aura of education and *pseudo* professionalism. There are many fools under these mantras.

There is really no substitute for taking personal responsibility in every area of our lives, including finance, health, and religion. Keep following a leader and you will eventually be in a ditch more like a human grave.

We sit on an economic powder keg. Authorities would have us to believe that the system will recover and prosper. There is no system. It is a patched-up paper money monster that has nothing left but confidence. When that falters, she blows!

The truth is we have eaten our seed corn! Not only that, we have borrowed from our future. Americans have been sold completely on the idea that lowering interest rates is the ticket to eternal material prosperity. Consequently, the American consumer has already borrowed from next year's consumption.

All speculative manias in history have led to financial excesses, overproduction capacities, and huge debt. This has led to a vicious downturn and financial busts which in turn has led to recessions or depressions.

The very salient point is that none of the financial establishment or public gurus saw the collapse coming now or in the past. The economic situation in the U.S. today is far more dangerous and complex than ever before. We are, indeed, faced with a fundamentally totally different set of economic, financial and now, geopolitical conditions than ever before in our economic history.

Inflation eventually creates deflation, as so well demonstrated in Japan. Ironically, deflation gives paper money more purchasing power, something governments never intend.

Inflation is an increase in the volume of money and credit relative to available goods. Deflation is a contraction in the volume of money relative to available goods. Simply put, deflation develops as a result of excessive debt built up during boom times. Almost no one expects deflation before it starts. And almost no one knows why deflation comes like a bolt out of the blue.

Here is the reason. The social mood reverses from euphoria to loss of confidence periodically. Why does the social mood reverse ever so often? The answer is because inflated economic activity and confidence burns out and reverses. Loss of confidence causes a collapse of credit which leads to substantial involuntary debt liquidation and many bankruptcies. If debt liquidation gets out of hand, the money stock collapses faster than it can be created as now.

The key to the next few years is to preserve your assets/savings and diversify. This means unequivocally to spread your assets. **Do not put all your eggs in one basket.**

A cash reserve in your possession is not all bad in case the printing presses fail to inflate as they intend to do. You can always change cash to gold coins.

Needless to say, debt is a bad thing in deflation. In fact, it's a disaster. Try to get rid of your debt now or as much as you can. This includes real estate debt.

When prices collapse as in the current Japanese deflation, cash and savings is king because as prices go down, cash becomes worth more and more.

■ Buy gold coins, especially one-ounce bullion coins, Gold American Eagles. Buy some "junk silver." That is U.S. 90 percent silver coins minted through 1964.

■ Buy Swiss francs in the form of a Swiss annuity.

■ Stash cash in U.S. dollars as long as we experience deflation or the threat of deflation.

■ Do not buy or hold stocks except some select quality gold stocks, i.e., Newmont, Royal Gold, Goldcorp, Agnico Eagle, Glamis Gold, Goldfields, Randgold, and/or Tocqueville Gold Fund.

Buy now and hold for the big advance coming soon. The top could be three to four years out. Then we will sell and buy the New York Stock Market again which will eventually arrive at rock bottom with historical values. Please remember that at that point, the world economy will look like a black hole and you will be scared to death.

In the meantime, the gold market will not go straight up. There will be corrections or shakeouts. Hold and build your position.

CHAPTER 7

The IRS and You

The US Federal Income Tax

A mericans believe that they have to pay income tax so the Federal Government can pay its bills. They believe that they are required to pay federal income tax.

The Truth—The Federal Government does not need your income tax but they have to have it! Please let me explain: Abraham Lincoln started the first income tax in America. Yes, ole Honest Abe had to print paper money to pay for the Civil War.

The income tax and paper money go together. One calls for the other. The paper money and income tax is well conceived and planned fraud. The generations that have been born into this deception never question it.

Here it is! John Maynard Keynes reveals the sordid plot in his 1920 book, *Economic Consequences of the Peace:* "If governments should refrain from regulation (taxation), the worthlessness of the (paper) money becomes apparent and the fraud can be concealed no longer."

So income tax hides the paper money scam. The people believe that they have to pay income tax to support the government. Not true!

The purpose of the income tax:

1. It is used to regulate the consumption of the people and to regulate the volume of paper money so that it does not become worthless too fast so as to be detected.

2. The income tax system is a pretense to snoop on every American.

3. Most of all, the income tax hides the fraud of paper money and the deception called government debt.

Almost nobody on the "animal farm" questions this. We have been tricked into the paper money scam and the income tax. As to the income tax, the people are tricked into "volunteering" and once they sign a 1040 income tax form, they are under merchant law and no longer under the U.S. Constitution.

You unknowingly waive your rights as you incriminate yourself by signing income tax forms. This is America.

Tracking Your Spending Habits

Plans for the IRS tracking all of your internet and credit card transactions are now in the works.

Credit card companies will help tax collections by reporting purchases to the IRS valued at $600 or more. Your purchasing habits can eventually entrap you.

The IRS is gearing up to do a "net worth" on everybody based on each "taxpayer's" spending profile. This means you may present the IRS with several large "tax deduction" expenses, whereupon the examiner will then calculate a "net worth" and conclude that your spending was greater than your income and slap on additional tax.

Unknown to the American people, Senator Charles Grassley (R-IA) is advocating a scheme to enlist more informants for the IRS by paying cash bounties to citizen snitchers who snitch on neighbors, clients, ex-friends, ex-spouses, etc. I don't know if the bounties would be "taxable."

The IRS, I read, already has 1,000 "controlled informants" (accountants) secretly on the IRS payroll. Well, what about all accountants and tax lawyers? The U.S. income tax system is entrenched. We are born into this involuntary servitude and few question it.

It was first started by Abraham Lincoln to tax "the wealthy." So it came and went a few times, but government and politicians can't resist the temptation. After all, the income tax is exactly one half of the paper money theft. You can't have one without the other.

The insiders have long understood that income tax can enslave the population without their ever knowing it. It can be accomplished by intimidation.

Taxes are very difficult to collect in hard money (gold and silver). People will not give up hard money for taxes and wars like they will with paper money.

They have been calling it democracy so long that people actually believe "paying our fair share" is patriotic. How has it happened without a revolution? Gradually.

Taxpayers Money

Taxpayers money is the definition of an overworked term. We could teach Goebels a thing or two!

When ALL the writers refer to "taxpayers money," they think that our taxes are "taxpayers money" and they are trying to tell the public that the government "wastes taxpayers money" and they actually believe this nonsense.

Now to set this illusion in concrete, the IRS does reduce the numbers (money) in our checking accounts when we authorize them to do so, via our 1040 tax return. But no one ever asks where the numbers (money) go when deleted from our checking accounts.

These numbers (money) do not go to Washington as taxes to pay anything. They go into the cyberspace of the IRS computers. All this is Orwellian doublethink.

Facts: The dollar is a myth. Oh, I know that we have green strips of paper in our pockets that we believe are dollars. The numbers on the green strips of paper are our "dollars." So what we "spend" every day are the numbers or the symbols on our green strips of paper.

Now if the government "wastes our tax dollars," what do they waste? Do they waste the numbers or computer symbols called dollars? How is it possible in the realm of reality to spend or waste numbers that can be created to infinity?

What absurd nonsense! Please, we should memorize this! Anything that can be created to infinity cannot be "spent or wasted."

To spend or to waste implies to exhaust or use up. These money symbols (numbers) that we think of every day as money have no substance in reality. We as individuals do "spend" numbers but ours are limited. Therefore, we can use the term spend or debt as it relates to anything except the Federal Government and their symbiotic partners, the banks.

So what does the IRS do? They reduce our consumption by reducing the numbers in our checking accounts. It is a system of economic regulation to conceal the fraud that modern money is numbers created without limit by government/bankers.

What else does this Orwellian system do? It transfers wealth to the "money creators."

How does a government make war on its own people? We said that modern money is numbers or symbols which can be created to infinity. Hold on to your hat! Theft through fiat occurs when the VOLUME of numbers (money) exceeds the production of goods and services.

This is called inflation. So, the government makes war on its own people by increasing the volume of money.

Individuals, cities, counties, and states cannot increase their money supply (more numbers) by creating more. Only the Federal Government, in symbiotic relationship with the banks, has this monopolistic power.

When this monopoly creates inflation it reduces the exchange value of all "dollars" in savings and circulation. Where does this reduction in savings and dollar assets go? It goes to the money creators, the people who increased the volume of money (numbers) into the system.

Nobody controls the VOLUME of money except the money creators. How do they get away with this? The answer is the ignorance of the people.

Through the manipulation of economic classes and racial conflict and the military industrial complex the money creators generate a constant clamor for higher volumes of money, small percentages of which are dispensed back to the poorer classes.

The poor people get a crumb and they are happy.

Social Security and Medicare are created with excess money (numbers) volume. They are Ponzi schemes. What makes this system work even for a day? It's a confidence system.

Most people still believe that it is honest and that it will last even though their store of value and the purchasing power of their "money" is decreasing constantly. The other reason that the system of fiat works for periods of time is that the VOLUME of money is regulated through taxation.

Estate taxes, income taxes, and all taxes reduce the volume of money which extends the system.

When the volume of money is expanded, there must be a serious way to keep reducing the volume. Taxes and wars extinguish the excess volume of money. Do we have taxes? Do we have perpetual wars?

Wars don't cost money, they extinguish surplus volumes of money. Wars would not be possible without fiat.

Modern money is witchcraft, but it can be understood in terms of volume whether it is gold or fiat. President James A. Garfield said, "Whoever controls the volume of money in any country is absolute master of all industry and commerce."

The IRS: A Perfect Expression of Police Power

Second only to the word democracy, the word "taxpayer" is an establishment word. The goal of the system is to get everyone to think of themselves as taxpayers. They know that as we think we are taxpayers, so shall we become.

People who believe that they are taxpayers have, in fact, become taxpayers. They lose all initiative to question those who question the income tax.

It is a modern star chamber and the only reason we are not totally humiliated is because we are manipulated to believe that we are "paying our fair share." This is another mind-altering phrase which is used to extract wealth from the American people. To whom are we "paying our fair share"—to immoral evil?

The income tax system is a sinister creation of organized crime called government. The IRS system is the perfect expression of police power because it operates as force; it extracts confession and forces self-incrimination of citizens.

Yet in its hypocrisy it persuades the public mind that it is, "A voluntary system of self-assessment." The IRS is a system that uses police power to force involuntary servitude. There is a parasite income tax system in America that prospers on the confusion and duplicity of the tax system by "helping" you comply.

Individuals and business expend millions of hours in an effort to comply with a system that President Reagan referred to as a system of voodoo and witchcraft.

The IRS is best described as a creation of benevolent total-itarianism. This means that the public is persuaded to accept tyranny because they assume that their response to the tax system is necessary. Add to this the fear and intimidation used by the IRS and the result is essentially an attitude of "got to pay my fair share."

Self-sacrifice is not synonymous with moral duty nor does it justify the accommodation of evil. The frivolous issue put forth and debated is whether or not the income tax is mandatory by law. No, it is not mandatory by law, but it is most definitely mandatory by force—police force. In the real world it does not matter what law requires. It matters what is required by force.

Our lives are dominated and consumed by the process and payment of taxes. It would be accurate to say that our existence is indexed to the tax system in America. Yet not one person in 10 million has the monetary understanding that income taxes have absolutely nothing to do with economic or financial support of the Federal Government.

The Federal Government does not need your income taxes to pay its bills. The income tax system (withholding) was inaugurated under the "crisis" of World War II in its present form. Before that time, not more than 1 percent of the American people paid any so-called tax on income. What did the government do for money all those years before World War II?

Modern money is numbers and abstraction. The government/central bank creates those numbers and "pays" the numbers, called dollars, for what it needs.

The monetary system of the United States is regulated by the IRS income tax system. The IRS income tax system implies in the public mind that the IRS is collecting taxes to support the Federal Government and pay its expenses. This is not true but it serves as a disguise to hide fraud.

What then is the IRS collecting? When you send your check to the IRS, the IRS then subtracts the numbers on your check from your checking account. In this action, the IRS is a regulator of your consumption. Your consumption of goods and services is reduced by the exact numbers.

The fiat monetary system would not work without the regulation of your consumption. This essential function of the IRS is the reason that it is a system backed by police power.

Does the IRS spend your numbers (dollars) or send them to Washington as taxes? No, they disappear in the reverse manner that they were created. The more numbers that disappear, the more the government can create without causing price inflation.

When the IRS reduces your numbers, your consumption is effectively transferred to government consumption. The most revealing statement ever printed which describes the IRS system and reveals the fraud is that found in the book published in 1919 entitled *Economic Consequences of the Peace,* by John Maynard Keynes.

Lord Keynes is the darling of modern bankers, politicians, and *pseudo* economists. We quote: "If government should refrain from regulation, (taxation) the worthlessness of the money becomes apparent and the fraud upon the people can be concealed no longer."

This statement clearly says that the income tax system covers the fraud that government prints its own money. The government does not need your numbers (dollars). It creates its own in unlimited amounts. But the people must believe that they are paying taxes according to "their fair share."

Confession and Self-Incrimination

People can be conditioned to accept anything. In time, people stop all questions and all inquiry. The few who do question the tax system become known as "tax protesters" and are labeled unpatriotic."

The propaganda machine has successfully persuaded the American people to think of themselves as "taxpayers." After all, you won't think bad thoughts about something you are.

The income tax is an illegal and moral evil that forces full disclosure of our lives to government authority. Income tax is more than disclosure. It is confession and self-incrimination.

In fact, it is impossible to file an income tax form without confession and self-incrimination. The IRS will not accept a 1040 tax return without a signature. Once it is signed, it is an enforceable contract that gives the IRS unilateral authority to force your confession or "testimony," (witness against yourself, which is illegal and unconstitutional), and to assess taxes, penalties, and interest. People are tricked by phrases like, "paying our fair share."

This is altruistic nonsense because no one can pay taxes with debt money. The income tax is a people control and information system. There is no better description of the income tax system than organized crime.

The IRS Trap

Floyd Wright says in his book, *Become a Nontaxpayer and Save,* that the greatest secret never told is that the American people have been conned into a contractual agreement with the Federal Government under the pretense of paying income taxes. He says that the reason that patriots have gotten entangled in the IRS trap is because they always have tried to use constitutional issues.

Mr. Wright says, "When we execute a 1040 form, we are executing a negotiable instrument. This makes us a merchant and as a merchant, the act of completing a 1040 form completes a contractual agreement and a contractual obligation. This act clearly puts us under the Uniform Commercial Code. Therefore, any pleadings based on the Constitution are frivolous and misplaced."

The American people are victims of a massive entrapment scheme that has conned them out of billions of dollars, as well as millions of hours of recordkeeping and loss of freedom. Federal judges and U.S. attorneys have all conspired against human rights by failing to inform the people of the nature of income tax entrapment.

Computer Notices... An IRS Bonanza

The IRS has developed a huge automated computer system that brings in billions of dollars. The system, like all IRS activity, operates on intimidation and bluff.

The IRS sends out tens-of-thousands of form computer notices every year demanding payment with no agent's name and little or no explanation on the computer letter. Most people pay or shortly they get follow-up computer letters demanding payment with assessments for interest and penalties.

Fully half of the collection notices according to Government Accounting Office (GAO) are phony or incorrect. The point is that the computer notice system does not allow for "taxpayer" response, questions, or explanations. And it circumvents the tax court process where there is at least a 60 percent chance to abate the tax. The IRS knows that you can't communicate with a computer. They can demand collections and never confront the "taxpayer."

Section 6213D of the IRS tax code allows the IRS to make assessments through automated computer notices that are not subject to deficiency procedures. Normal deficiency procedures allow a taxpayer a hearing as to the facts in tax court. Deficiency procedures are related to the normal audit but not to computer notices that demand immediate payment.

There is an exception in favor of the taxpayer in Section 6213D of the tax code. But of course, few people know about it and act within the 60-day allotted time period. If you respond in writing and demand cancellation and abatement of the alleged tax liability, the IRS has to cancel the tax and issue a deficiency notice if there is really a tax due.

Do not ask questions or bring up other issues. Simply demand abatement of the tax. This stops the tax demand for immediate payment and allows for the normal tax court deficiency process. All income tax procedures and so-called tax law is in truth merchant law. It is not constitutional law.

This means that all IRS notices must be responded to or the taxpayer becomes subject to assessment and collection procedures. It quickly becomes an entangled nightmare and unless one is judgment proof, the IRS can and will collect as they are backed by real and present police power.

CHAPTER 8

Privacy and Asset Protection

Keep a Low Profile... The Government Is Targeting Your Assets

We worry about the criminal element stealing and plundering our property and our homes. This is child's play compared to government seizure under the pretense of "asset forfeiture" at all levels of government.

Government agents at the federal, state, or local level can seize any of your property, as "probable cause," if they suspect it has been used in the commission of a crime. The government is looting outright under the color of the law.

As others have discovered, an honest, law-abiding citizen can easily become a target for asset forfeiture. **Don't go to sleep on this one.**

Sadly, our best protection as an American is privacy and keeping a low profile. This means many things. It means talking less to friends and neighbors about your assets. It means not displaying your wealth to envious government agents, friends, or neighbors.

■ Consider a Swiss annuity as an out-of-the-country, non-reportable savings account.

■ Think about changing paper or financial assets into physical assets such as gold, silver, and platinum, and keep them in your possession.

■ Transfer your assets to heirs as much as possible over time, while you are still living.

■ Be careful about disclosing medical records to insurance companies or anyone else. The Medical Information Bureau (MIB) is fast getting a medical dossier on every American. No, you don't have to disclose as much as you think.

■ Be extremely sensitive about your bank transactions and your bank records. They are open to the IRS or any government agency under any pretense. Many people recycle personal and company checks outside the banking system. (Example: X pays Y with a check and Y uses the check to pay Z.) This is legal.

■ If you need help in your office or business, consider independent contractors. This gets you out of a lot of bureaucratic nonsense and gives the contractor a Schedule C (IRS form) to help in their business deductions. It is mutually beneficial when this arrangement is possible.

■ If you are interested in overseas banking, choose a bank that does not have U.S. branches. Some banks issue offshore credit cards. Most will take properly endorsed second party checks or paychecks for deposit, just as U.S. banks do.

Authority depends upon and has its existence based upon your disclosure of your assets, the nature of and source of your "income" and what manner of consumption, i.e., "your expense deductions."

Since government is of a parasite nature, it cannot exist without a host (the people). Therefore, it must operate a system to subdue its host through deception. Government must, if possible, extract wealth and labor on a "volunteer" basis. The separation of you and your assets begins with your volunteering information. Information is to government what blood is to a vampire.

The American people know next to nothing about low profile. Being low profile simply means not displaying wealth or high living and keeping your mouth shut.

Many naive people who love to flaunt their materialism have paid big time when the IRS decided to do a net worth audit on them. If the IRS bureaucrats decide to get you, they simply add up the value of all your visible assets. If they decide you possess

Homeland Security Out of Control

"Homeland Security" is a new phase of government out of control. U.S. authority is at war with the American people under the pretense of "war on terrorism." This strategy is an age old Machiavellian system of building up external fear and using the emergency as an excuse for all kinds of domestic suppression.

What to expect:
- More censorship.
- Jailed dissidents.
- Expropriated property.
- More nationalization of bankrupt companies.
- Expropriation of savings and retirement funds with currency debasement (the massive creation of "money").

How will the American people respond?
- People will finally dump the currency for gold/silver and barter.
- "Tax evasion" will escalate.
- Silent and open civil disobedience.
- Vast increase of political dissidence.
- Mistrust in government will spark bank runs as government freezes all bank accounts.
- Open hostility in the streets.

more assets than your income should afford, they can calculate your net worth and charge taxes on what you own, regardless of your income.

Someone may have given you money, cars, or real estate, but try to explain this to snooping bureaucrats who think what you have is theirs. The United States of America is the world leader for invading your privacy. No other country, past or present, comes close, and this includes Nazi Germany. Not many Americans really know this. The reason is that the government itself keeps a low profile on its invasion of your privacy.

The people control system plays people off against each other according to their capacity to deal with reality. The underlying problem is the implicit trust of authority. People believe what the politicians and the bureaucrats say almost without question. I have often wondered what kind of shock it would take to wake the American people up.

If you have anything and don't want your possessions taken from you through suit-happy lawyers or the government, you should become conscious of being low profile and make yourself as invisible as possible. The time is NOW to do this!!!

Your Bank is Spying on You

He who possesses the currency of the realm is suspect. Having cash or asking for cash money (currency) at your local bank can get you investigated or arrested.

"Know Your Customer" requirements turn your friendly banker into a surveillance agent for the government. Your banker can be held criminally accountable for failure to report any "suspicious" activities.

Be careful how much cash you withdraw from one bank at a time. You can become guilty of a financial crime and trigger a "Suspicious Activities Report," which is accessible to over a dozen agencies including the FBI, IRS, Secret Service, bank regulators, and state law enforcement. Banks are prohibited from informing customers when suspicious transaction reports have been filed on them.

The authorities can seize your bank account and your assets. They can seize your real and personal property.

Of course the excuse for the ongoing restriction of personal privacy and personal liberty is always crime. The government promotes crime and then uses crime to restrict your liberty. Government oppression under the color of law is to reduce the freedom of honest citizens. Criminals and crooks pay no attention to laws. Any child knows this.

Cash money offers a certain privacy and freedom of movement and choice. The underground economy operates on cash and barter. This puts it out of reach of bureaucrats and non-producing government parasites who want to live off of your labor.

Protect Yourself from Bank Snoops

Do you have sufficient unencumbered assets that would make you an attractive target for a lawsuit? The litigation explosion has spawned a new industry: Companies hired to snoop into your financial accounts to find assets to seize.

While the government has access to financial databases that can target your financial accounts, ordinary creditors don't— unless they have an "in" with police (some do).

They use various techniques to get this information, including:

■ Sending fake rebate checks for your endorsement. When you deposit the checks, they get your bank account number from the cancelled check.

■ Calling you and offering a pre-approved line of credit. To qualify, you must reveal your Social Security number, date of birth, and bank account numbers. Once investigators have this information, they contact the bank posing as you to determine your account balance.

If you have sufficient unencumbered assets, you then may be named in a lawsuit. To avoid being targeted in these schemes, never cash a rebate check from an unknown sender. Nor should you ever disclose personal information over the telephone to an unknown caller.

Notify your bank that you do not want account information disclosed over the phone, or at least not without a code word that confirms your identity.

Incidentally, information about offshore holdings almost never turns up in a casual asset search.

How to Protect Your Retirement Nest Egg

There is a definite pattern of government control and regulation of pension funds going on. We are sucked in with income tax gimmickry and then forfeit our pensions and savings in our retirement years.

The point is that none of the stated reasons for increased controls and regulations relate to the truth, nor will any of the excuses for confiscation.

The Solution:

1. According to your own understanding of government morality, you may consider getting out by paying penalties and taxes. At least stop paying in.

2. If you are 59 1/2 now, you might consider starting annual distributions.

3. Look into the possibility of a self-trusted plan where you are the trustee and custodian of your plan assets. Seek legal advice.

4. Take possession of all financial assets as far as possible, including stock certificates.

5. Retirement accounts are not taxable until terminated. Consider borrowing against your account up to the maximum when and where possible. Start getting information on this now.

6. A private gold plan. Accumulate gold, platinum, or silver coins and sell them off selectively as retirement needs demand and market prices are favorable.

7. Finally, invest in a Swiss annuity. These are the best for privacy and safety. Also, in a Swiss annuity, you will have currency switching privileges that will allow you to switch between Swiss francs, U.S. dollars, German marks, and the British pound.

Privacy Tactic: Look Overseas

For privacy, some Americans buy and sell stocks through foreign banks. In general it is not a complicated procedure.

There are varying requirements with different banks.

As a starter, Lloyds Bank in London accepts American accounts; $1,500 minimum. I do not consider this a high requirement.

They will issue credit cards, but probably not to new accounts until a track record is established. There is a lot of magic in a foreign credit card.

You can trade in or out of the country with practically no currency exchange cost. Also, you can pay your monthly statement with mutual fund checks or salary checks which are properly endorsed, all of this outside the U.S. banking system. I know of no law against this.

Keep your financial assets such as stock certificates in your physical possession instead of in street name at your broker. Many brokers are doing strange things. Brokerage houses almost insist on keeping our stocks in "street name."

Swiss Annuities as a Private Safety Net

Many have asked if Swiss annuities must be reported as a foreign financial account. The answer is "no" as of now. The reason is that annuities the world over are purchased from insurance companies.

Annuities are not life insurance policies because anyone can get them at any age regardless of one's health. Since annuities are purchased from insurance companies, they are not classed as financial accounts and are therefore not reportable on income tax returns.

Swiss annuities, just like American annuities, accumulate tax-free until withdrawal. The earnings are then taxable. Swiss annuities do not have seven to 10 year surrender charges, as do American annuities. A Swiss annuity is much like a bank account with a penalty for withdrawal of the account within the first year of 500 Swiss francs. Swiss annuities are out of reach of creditors, lawsuits, and the taxman provided your spouse or your children are the beneficiaries.

Many people around the world who are fearful of exchange controls, asset confiscation and bureaucratic tyranny have chosen the Swiss annuity as a safety net.

Watch Your Trash

Trash set out for collection in the United States is not protected from warrant-less search.

CHAPTER 9

The Legal System
Fire Your Lawyer!

Incompetent lawyers can ruin you. The trouble is you don't usually know what's happening until it's too late. Most run-of-the-mill lawyers are lazy. They don't do their (your) homework. They are grossly negligent.

Before you take the legal services of an attorney for granted please consider that all lawyers are not created equal as people naively assume. They are stratified—vast differences in ability and experience. Lawyers are really parasites on the system they created. They win whether you are the plaintiff or defendant unless, of course, your case is on contingency.

If you don't like the system (cover name "democracy") you can blame the lawyer cult, because they created it for themselves and the system. The system is not 100 percent lawyers, but almost, including all the way up to the Supreme Court. The history of America is a history of lawyers manipulating the system toward and in favor of federal power.

According to the book, *Sweet Land of Liberty,* by Henry Holzer, all significant issues in America since its founding fathers were decided (manipulated) in favor of the Federal Government and federal power.

Every issue is decided on the psychodrama of social conditioning. If you think certain thoughts negative to the system, and they can be drawn out, you will lose every time. Never let the system know what you are thinking. You have to speak in the prescribed thought control manner.

Lawyers carry the torch of cultural conditioning. They are

bound to the system, controlled by the system, and owe their existence and livelihood to the system. No matter what's in their hearts, they have to play the game. Most of them want to anyway because that's where the bucks are.

Never forget that all lawyers are officers of the court. This simply means that when the chips are down, the house wins with every lawyer on the side of the court and the court represents the system, not you.

Before you go to retain a lawyer formulate some questions. Is there a similar case on the books? How was it decided? What legal points of law are involved? Is the jurisdiction favorable to your cause of action? How long will it take the lawyer to file suit? What is the statute of limitations? Should your lawyer associate another lawyer who has a "better spin" on your case?

A man who throws stones cannot live in a glass house. Ask every question you can think of and look up words and terms in *Black's Law Dictionary*. Take responsibility for your case. The more you learn, the more you can evaluate how your lawyer is doing on your case.

If you don't feel good, fire your lawyer and get another one. Forget *pro se!* The system looks upon *pro se* with contempt.

If you want to win in the king's court, let the king think of you as his subject, not a rebel. You may have to think one thing and do another. Such are the times.

Do You Trust Your Attorney? Think Twice.

You can no longer absolutely depend on attorney-client privilege. Attorneys who become informants against their clients do not necessarily violate attorney-client privilege.

The U.S. Department of Justice has publicly defended using attorneys as informants as a perfectly valid law enforcement tool. The "War on Crime" is an excuse for war on Americans. You can be a victim of civil forfeiture and never be charged with a crime. Federal agents or local police can seize virtually everything you own if you are "suspected" of a financial crime—not being able to account for the source of your wealth. Or if your property has been used or suspected of being used in the commission of a crime, it can be seized even if you are unaware of any wrongdoing.

In the U.S. there are 300 federal statutes on civil forfeiture designed to target property. Civil forfeiture laws allow governments to seize property with virtual impunity. Yes, this is so in America.

CHAPTER 10

Restoring and Maintaining Your Health

No matter how successful we are at amassing wealth and holding on to it, we cannot enjoy it fully unless we are also sound in body and mind and maintain good health. To that end, Bob Livingston has devoted untiring efforts toward identifying the many dangers to our health posed by modern life and raising alarms when needed. At the same time, Bob has invested untold hours rooting out secrets of restoring our health and keeping healthy through proactive alternatives to the conventional medical dogmas. The highlights of these gems of health wisdom that follow will help you live healthy, be well, and enjoy your wealth.

Why Krill Oil?

In krill, we may have the most basic nutrition possible. The point is that when we consume krill and krill oil we are at the very beginning of the marine food chain. This is our guarantee of purity, as well as peak nutrition.

Krill oil means bioavailability for peak absorption. The key is the phytoplankton diet of the tiny krill. The smaller the marine life is, the shorter its life span and the purer from contamination. So, the smaller the sea life the less mercury and other toxins it contains.

In fact, phytoplankton is grown abundantly in oceans around the world and is the foundation of the marine life food chain.

Krill's food source is phytoplankton. Since phytoplankton contains the pigment chlorophyll, which gives them their greenish color, its food source comes from photosynthesis in which sunlight is the energy source.

Through photosynthesis, phytoplankton are also responsible for much of the oxygen present in the earth's atmosphere. What better energy food source than sunlight? Besides photosynthesis, phytoplankton are crucially dependent on ocean minerals. These are primarily macronutrients such as nitrate, phosphate, or salicylic acid. This means that through krill we are getting the macro-nutrients and microorganisms in aquatic food webs of the ocean, as well as in sea salt which we have come to accept as a miracle for human health.

So we are talking about a phytoplankton food chain which is the essential ecological function for all aquatic life. Two-thirds of all the photosynthesis on earth occurs in the oceans.

Krill oil is an excellent source of Omega-3. A major health issue in the United States today is obesity, caused in large part by our diet heavy in Omega-6. In early human history the ratio of Omega-6 to Omega-3 fats was one to one (1:1). In America today, our dietary ratio is as high as 50 to one in favor of Omega-6 fats. The lower our ratio of Omega-6 to Omega-3 the better, ideally one to one (1:1).

Many scientists believe that a major reason for our high incidence of heart disease, hypertension, diabetes, obesity, premature aging, and some forms of cancer is the profound imbalance of our consumption of Omega-6 and Omega-3 fatty acids.

The large food processors, in their drive for mass marketing and shelf life, have loaded us with Omega-6 fatty acids. They have given us easy living and early death.

There are more oils on the market to avoid than to eat. Commercial oils to avoid are sunflower, corn, soy, safflower, and canola. We should be alert to eat no hydrogenated or partially hydrogenated fats, no margarine, no vegetable oils, and no shortening. All these are chock full of Omega-6 fats and have worsened our ratio of good/bad fats. Grain-fed beef is very high in the bad fats.

Oils that are good are high quality virgin olive oil and coconut oil. Also good are avocados and organic butter from grass-fed cows.

Can we just eat fish? Yes, and over time we can begin to

reverse our Omega ratio, especially if we greatly diminish our intake of Omega-6 and increase our intake of Omega-3.

Krill oil is the perfect way to restore proper Omega-3/Omega-6 balance, as it contains 10 times more healthy Omega-3 fatty acids than Omega-6. This is more than enough to help offset the dangers of the high Omega-6 American diet and will greatly help you reduce inflammation.

Krill oil is purely formulated from very small-sized Antarctic krill which feed on the powerful phytoplankton sea diet.

In the past we have discussed the huge problem of blood in seniors turning to sludge. Our blood thickens with age, evidently leading to a stroke or heart attack. Omega-3 deficiency is known to compromise the blood-brain barrier, which normally protects the brain from unwanted matter gaining access to the brain. Omega-3 deficiency can also decrease normal blood flow in the brain.

Just for the record, clinical studies are conclusive that Omega-3s improve heart health, improve memory, slow aging, and support the brain and nervous system.

Krill oil contains phospholipids that closely resemble the ones in the human brain and makes krill oil very easy for the body to assimilate and use. Contrary to this, regular fish oil contains triglycerides which the body has to break down and convert before assimilation.

I've been a long-time advocate of supplementing diets with fish oil. However, I firmly believe that krill oil is a remarkable discovery and will totally revolutionize the fish oil and Omega-3 market as we know it. In every head-to-head scientific study between fish oil and krill oil, krill has been proven far superior in its healthy benefits. It's definitely made a believer out of me.

Commercial "Food" Processors More Dangerous to Americans Than an Occupational Standing Army

I just want to share a tidbit with you that should make you furious. It's fructose corn syrup; more dangerous than a hydrogen bomb, but more profitable than a money machine.

So-called fructose corn syrup is not fructose. It is not corn and it is not syrup. It is a synthetic sugar made from various things like sulfuric acid and sawdust. If you read labels, you won't find many manufactured foods that don't have it as an ingredient and most of the time, the first ingredient.

Fructose corn syrup is a cheap filler with no nutrition, only calories. It is a non-food, not fit for human consumption but has been heavy on the market for about 80 years.

In the past, it was not allowed in Canada—I don't know about now.

Fructose corn syrup achieves three things:

1. It blocks the assimilation of calcium. Ever heard of the osteoporosis epidemic in America? Most Americans chase their calcium with fructose corn syrup. Almost everyone over age 50 suffers a dangerous loss of calcium.

2. It's only fructose corn syrup that will cause cancer in test animals— are we test animals?

3. Predisposes humans to cancer. Fructose corn syrup is a synthetic sugar that causes the bypassing of the pancreas. This shuts the pancreas down, causing a nation of diabetics. Harvey Wiley, the first head of the Bureau of the Chemist (later to become the FDA) warned of the deceptive marketing of fructose corn syrup and that it would cause a nation of diabetics.

Well, has it happened? Start reading labels. Fructose corn syrup (synthetic sugar) is in everything!

Healthy Children!

Beautiful healthy children without broken bones and all the childhood viruses is a present reality.

Yes, it can be! We need four things to build strong bones and immunity without vaccinations. They are calcium lactate, whole complex vitamin C, vitamin F, and vitamin D. If children (or adults) have adequate levels of this foursome, there would be no childhood sickness due to viruses or infection; i.e., peak immunity.

Our So-Called "Health Care" System

Boy, what a mis-named scam! The current disease-oriented money system is collapsing. It should as it is the greatest cause of sickness and death in the history of the world.

Medicine, as the public knows it, is dying. It is now in terminal phase. It is a system of conflict of interest, tainted research, greed for money, deceived and pretentious doctors and scientists, lying, cheating, invasion by the morally bankrupt marketing automatons of the drug industry, greedy power hungry politicians, and federal and state regulators.

It is all about money generated on the sick and the dying.

The sick care industry is not only profiting from the sick and dying, it is the greatest cause of sickness and premature death.

And it is a U.S. Government industry. It is sponsored and financed by the U.S. Government. There would not be a single hospital in the United States without federal funny money and the insurance business.

If you had to pay a doctor out of your pocket, he would have to produce something besides a palliative. He couldn't fake it with drugs and surgery. It all happens because the people don't know the difference in health care and sick care.

Millions are now beginning to take responsibility for their own health.

I apologize for the simplicity of this rather inexpensive protocol. There would never be fever and colds.

But if they occur, there is a deficit of the above four or some or one of them. If a child develops fever, it is deficient of the above and probably all of them. Please stick to the protocol of calcium lactate, whole vitamin C complex (not ascorbic acid), vitamin F, and vitamin D. Normally, whole complex C will stop a fever by itself.

If not, add calcium lactate. Same with adults. When children break bones, they may have plenty of calcium, but it's not diffused for lack of vitamin F. It takes vitamin F to get calcium into the tissue and bones.

American Fascism and "Health Regulations"

The few of you who know a little Italian history under Mussolini have an idea about fascism. Fascism is simply a marriage of the state and big business and the people are the pawns.

My mother used to say that, "What you don't know won't hurt you." Boy was she ever wrong! Believe me; what you don't know is fatal to your health and your children's health.

There is no better example of fascism than American pharmaceuticals and their silent partners, the giant food processors. These oligopolies have mounted the most aggressive attack on our health.

We're talking red alert! While we are all in love with our materialism, the big rats have advanced on all fronts with murder incorporated. These people have no morals and the government sanctions this fraud.

Why do you think that drug companies average spending 12 percent on research and 40 percent on advertising? Advertising can easily be defined as propaganda designed to get you to eat something or take something against your health. And what's more, they have a new thrust at little children.

Well, it doesn't take long to build a conditioned response in a child's mind. And when parents are ignorant, there is a double crisis. Big business with its vast resources is unbridled in its new attack on the whole family. We are sitting ducks.

The whole population—from brand new infants to very old people—has already submitted to every conceivable vaccination. Now there is a huge program to check all kids for "high cholesterol" and high blood pressure.

Well, can you guess their angle? They want everybody on their drugs. And the fast food industry has prepared the way.

Every kid on the block has his daily fast food box (trans-fatty acids) which triggers all diseases.

And now the number one cause of death for kids ages one through 15 and adults ages 25 to 40 is CANCER. Our juvenile diet of fast foods (trans-fatty acids) has caused an obesity epidemic to hit toddlers and kids as young as four who have high insulin levels, a precursor to diabetes, and high blood pressure causing abnormal liver function.

Even *Forbes* magazine (no friend of yours) related ("J & J's dirty little secret") how Johnson & Johnson decided it was cheaper to pay a few million dollars for adults and children who had died from Tylenol® than it would be to warn of the potential lethal side effects and scare away customers.

Every home should have a *Physician's Desk Reference* and look up everything they intend to take or give their children.

Johnson & Johnson is also the company that brought us Olestra, so that you can eat "guilt free, fat-free" trans-fatty acid laden pretzels and potato chips like Pringles®.

Olestra inhibits the absorption of not only fat, but all of your fat soluble vitamins (A, D, E, K, beta carotene, CoQ10, and lipoic acid) that protect you from cancer, heart disease and everything else.

So you get the trans-fatty acid "foods" plus the Olestra to finish off your nutritional capacity. Is this deception and fraud? Try to do something about it!

Meanwhile, Johnson & Johnson is spending $40 million to push their new eight-hour Tylenol® on children. Deaths from Tylenol® are because it's extremely toxic to the liver in low or "normal" doses.

The toxicity compounds in children and seniors who both have less detoxification ability. So Johnson & Johnson is buying ads in *Rolling Stone* and *Runner's World* to target young people and children. Saddam Hussein never did this to us!

Health Wisdom

Want a real gem of health wisdom that few people have ever heard of? Our bodies have a far harder time processing food than we can imagine.

Overeating causes impaired metabolism leading to insulin resistance and abdominal obesity and inflammation. How serious is this?

The answer is that they are markers for heart disease and cancer. When food intake is excessive (not necessarily a glutton) particularly foods with a lot of empty calories which we call nonfoods, there is tremendous metabolic stress.

Myth:

Studies in which rats are restricted in their calorie intake but not in their nutrient intake have repeatedly shown that these animals live up to 40 percent longer than rats allowed to eat as usual or all they wanted.

And not only do these calorie-restricted rats live longer, they also live better; that is, they are protected from developing the usual diseases of aging, such as arthritis, diabetes, dementia, and cancer.

They also look great with thick, shiny coats, full sets of whiskers, and shiny eyes. On top of this, they run through mazes as well as much younger rats.

The same result was achieved with a variety of test animals. Less food and more nutrition! This means to leave off the empty nonfood calories because this is what we eat the most of, and this is exactly what is destroying our health.

Problem is most people don't know the difference in nonfood or empty food calories and nutrition. They think that they are the same. Food is food, right?

No, it's far from right. It's called full-belly starvation. We eat, we feel full and even satisfied, but we are slowly starving.

Most all the illness today is a manifestation or end result of slow starvation, meaning too many calories and little or not enough nutrition. Our hunger mechanism gets fooled just the same as our thirst mechanism breaks down and we unknowingly dehydrate. So most people are malnourished as well as dehydrated.

There was a food shortage in Germany after World War I so sawdust was added to their food. At first they added a very small percent. Then they gradually increased until the people became malnourished and sick. All the time they had full bellies. They did not feel hungry.

When a person eats a fast food hamburger most of that hamburger is a nonfood or calories only. The bread is bleached flour and the meat is full of antibiotics and growth hormones. They have sold billions because they taste good to many people.

Let me give you an example: We eat about a thimble full of nutrition a day and at least a quart or two of just calories. It's the calories that cause disease and aging.

Believe me, our bodies will adjust on much less food, especially if we drink the required amount of water.

Some of the best human evidence of the calorie-reduction concept sprang from the Biosphere II experiments. Here eight men and women lived in a self-sustaining enclosed environment in the Arizona desert for two years, growing or raising all their own food, producing their own oxygen, making their own water, and processing their own waste.

Because the amount of food they could produce was limited, they ended up on a calorie-restricted diet. After the two years were up, the men had lost about 18 percent of their body weight; the women had lost 10 percent. And every measurable variable (body fat, blood pressure, exercise capacity, oxygen consumption, blood sugar levels, cholesterols, cortisol levels, white blood counts, and so on) showed by every measurable parameter that these people had become substantially younger than when they entered the environment two years earlier.

The reason for this? By consuming fewer calories, they experienced a much lower level of oxidative stress. This is all too convincing to ignore.

I assume that our readers know the difference in nonfood calories and nutrition. Sounds like this would solve any diet or health problem.

Soft Drinks are Slow Killers.
You Think Iraq is Bad, Listen to This!

Sugar grabs oxygen with the highest priority.

Most commercial foods are full of sugar. Soft drinks are not soft. They are hard killers. They're highly acid with an average pH of 2.5. That much acid will dissolve anything.

Younger people are becoming highly acidic and are being hit by so-called adult diseases. There are no warnings on the containers. Where is the FDA?

Higher alkalization means more oxygen and more oxygen signifies higher immunity. Is this simple? This makes inoculations nonsense! Alkaline water will dissolve acid waste much quicker because of the higher pH.

No Health Without Nutrition

The nutritional relationship to health is blacked-out and erased from public memory. The entire medical monopoly—the "sickness industry"—is based on malnutrition. Its foundation is deception and misinformation about nutrition.

The facts and objective reality don't count with programmed minds. Using chemicals (drugs) to heal is every bit witchcraft and superstition as was the bloodletting that killed George Washington. Yes, at one time blood letting was "orthodox medicine."

Education itself becomes a conspiracy against health and nutrition when the learned, educated, and professional class is neutralized against common sense and objective reality. "Science" becomes a mask and charade for cover up of the medical monopoly.

A peculiar trait of the "educated" man is that he cannot accept anything beyond the parameters of his "training." A formally educated mind has neither the ability nor the inclination to appraise the merits of anything new and innovative.

Certain basic changes in our conditioned response to health must be recognized:

1. Big business has a vested interest in sickness, not wellness. There is a sickness industry in America and it is jealously protected.
2. Responsibility for your health begins with you.
3. Drugs do not and cannot heal. Only your body can heal itself provided it has the right fuel.
4. Drugs are palliatives. They mask the symptoms of disease without effecting a cure.
5. All degenerative disease is a form of malnutrition and starvation. Disease is not a drug deficiency.
6. Synthetic "vitamins" are not nutrition or food supplements. They are drugs.
7. Most food that we eat is commercial "food." It has calories and it produces energy but no nutrition. This means that we can have a full belly and be starving to death. When body reserves are depleted, degenerative disease sets in. There is mass starvation in America. The most common non-vitamin foods are sugar, white flour, white rice, and macaroni or pasta products. These are prominent in the American diet, constituting about 90 percent of total food intake. These are commercial "foods" because they can be stored and shipped because of the fact that they are devitalized and devitaminized. All these are energy-producing foods that contain no building materials for the body. The consequences of consuming these so-called foods are susceptibility to infections, enlarged tonsils, cavities (decayed) teeth, unruly and hyper-disposition, stunted growth, rickets, and permanent damage to many of the organs of the body.
8. Hippocrates taught that natural food is the best medicine and that food, not drugs, heal.
9. Deficiency disorders cause disease which carries to the next generation, causing a tendency toward race degeneration.
10. Good food is perishable food as opposed to devitalized, sterilized, and denatured commercial foods.

Conclusion: Good nutrition and quality of life are synonymous. Good nutrition includes whole-raw foods, whole-food complexes and all-natural vitamin supplement complexes. Good nutrition prevents premature senility and can possibly increase the average lifespan 15 to 20 years. Wrinkles, obesity, edema, and grossness of the features can be mostly avoided.

Acidosis and Nutrition

"All deaths from so-called natural causes are merely the end-point of progressive acid saturation. There is no such thing as natural death," says Dr. George W. Crile. What a simple truth that almost anyone can understand but almost nobody does. It is critically important!

Acidosis precedes and provokes all sickness and disease. Acidosis or an acid reaction is anything consumed as food that has a reaction in the body below a pH of 7.

The well body succumbs to physical disorders when its own acid debris accumulates to the point where resistance is broken down and the body consequently becomes susceptible to infection, cold, fatigue, or exhaustion. Sickness is a house-cleaning process that takes various forms: Diarrhea, headache, colds, skin eruptions, abscesses, arthritis, fevers, etc. All spring from a common cause — an accumulation of acid waste in the body.

Enzyme activity in the tissues is regulated by pH levels. Enzymes that are constructive in nature that normally build tissues will reverse their activity and begin to tear down tissue in the event of a pH drop (i.e. acid).

In acidosis, the outstanding clinical symptom is lack of oxygen. This of course directly relates to the strophanthin research that reveals that heart attacks are not caused by occlusions but by hyperacidity of the blood. The occlusion comes after the heart attack.

Heart attacks are associated with anoxia or lack of oxygen. Couple the epidemic of heart disease with the very high acid diet of Americans and the mystery begins to be unveiled.

Everyone knows the exponential growth of Americans' consumption of refined sugar. Well, refined sugar is a major promoter of acidosis. The point is that our daily diet is becoming increasingly acid.

The same conclusion applies to our epidemic of cancer. The late Dr. Max Gerson pulled terminal patients from the dead by quickly reversing the hyperacidity of their condition.

Specifically, he fed them eight to 10 glasses per day of raw carrot juice. Carrot juice rapidly corrected their acid conditions and they immediately began to rally.

How so? Carrots contain essential alkalis—calcium, sodium, magnesium, and potassium in abundance. Secondly, carrots contain a great quantity and quality of anti-infective vitamin A.

Dr. Gerson used other things too, but raw carrot juice was essential to his program. If you are not a "juicing" person, try 100 percent natural carrot juice powder. It is the closest thing to real carrot juice available.

What to Do: Learn now how to balance your diet with 80 percent alkaline foods and only 20 percent acid foods.

Malnutrition and Physical Degeneration

When Americans see little emaciated malnourished black African children being used by the TV media for the solicitation of funds for starving children, few of them, if any at all, understand starvation.

There are two kinds of starvation. One of course is simply not enough food. The second is far more insidious, and that is plenty of food with no nutrition.

Our concern is the second one because this applies to almost every American. It is by far the most deceptive and widespread disaster in history. It is more threatening to our national interest than would be an invading army.

And not one person suspects it. When we as a nation have full bellies, it is all but impossible to convince Americans that we are starving to death.

The problem is that full belly starvation is an oxymoron. It contradicts simple logic until we get a basic understanding of nutrition. This deception is compounded if we look at the exploding size and height of each generation. The explanation for this is the massive amount of growth hormones put in beef and fowl food. Forced growth is not nutrition.

The elements of human health are calories, energy, and nutrition. With the American diet, we are only getting calories and energy. There is little or no nutrition in the American diet.

There is literally an invisible famine in the land. The American civilization is a failure. It's a commercial secret that food processors don't want known. Our inferior diet is causing social decay and race deterioration.

Donald Laird says in his book, *The Tail that Wags the Nation,* "The country's average level of general ability sinks lower with each generation." Dr. Weston Price says in his classic work, *Nutrition and Physical Degeneration,* "The problem of the relation of physical defects to delinquency, in its various phases, including major crime, constitutes one of the most alarming aspects of our modern problems in social degeneration."

C. F. Chassell in his book, *Relation Between Morality and Intellect,* states that, "The correlation between delinquency and mental inferiority as found in the case of feeble-minded groups is clearly positive, and tends to be marked in degree."

C. L. Burt wrote in *The Young Delinquent,* "There is a direct relationship between delinquency and physical degeneration."

All this is to say that there is positive research that we are having a constant racial and mental degeneration, a progressive dumbing down correlated with rising crime and deteriorating morality. Physical and mental degeneration is directly related to nutritional deficiency. This truth is politically taboo and you will never hear anything about it.

The Thyroid is Related to Cholesterol Metabolism

Blood cholesterol is elevated in persons with a lower-functioning thyroid.

The gland depends upon iodine for its normal function. Without iodine the thyroid cannot produce its hormone, thyroxine.

When the thyroid is not supplied with sufficient iodine there is an increase in the size of the thyroid gland, a condition called "goiter." This can be reduced by simply taking iodine.

So when the thyroid is overactive there is a calcium loss; when the thyroid is underactive, we have cholesterol accumulation.

We can measure our own thyroid balance by taking underarm basal temperature for about five days in a row. This means taking morning temperature underarm before we get out of bed in the morning.

Normal body temperature is 98.6 degrees. If it is below this as much as one degree we likely need more iodine and/or thyroxin in the form of Armour Dessicated Hormone.

Do not take a synthetic thyroid hormone such as most doctors prescribe.

Your Thyroid and Your Heart: Low basal temperature mentioned above means low basal metabolism which controls the rate at which each cell burns the food that gives us energy.

This directly relates to our quality of life because thyroid deficiency may mimic a disease. For this reason every man, woman and child should test their basal (at rest) body temperature.

About half of the population suffers from some degree of thyroid deficiency. Most allopathic doctors ignore thyroid function and when they do test function, they do so with a blood profile which most of the time does not pick up low thyroid function.

If thyroid function is to be treated it usually is a lifetime protocol. Hypothyroidism (low thyroid function) is serious but is very easy to detect with the self basal temperature test. And it is equally easy to treat.

Doctors will start hypothyroid patients on very low doses (about 0.5 grain) and build up over months. The first hint of the connection of heart disease with low thyroid function (hypo-thyroidism) came when investigators demonstrated that elevated cholesterol could be brought down to normal with thyroid therapy.

Thyroid therapy does reduce the rate of formation of athero-sclerosis in the heart arteries. I never heard or read where an allopathic cardiologist observed or knew this.

Broda O. Barnes, M.D., Ph.D, concluded after thousands of case histories that the hypothyroid patient at a young age or any age is unusually susceptible to heart attacks.

Even in the hypothyroid infant, atherosclerosis starts. Dr. Barnes says that atherosclerosis results from thyroid deficiency and not from the elevated serum fats that accompany it.

He said that 95 percent of the cholesterol levels returned to normal with only thyroid therapy. I recommend the book, *Solved: The Riddle of Heart Attacks,* by Broda O. Barnes, M.D., Ph.D.

Long-Term Effects of Immunizations

A vaccination is a method by which diluted disease agents are introduced into the system by avoiding the natural defense mechanisms of the body. They are in a sense, parachuted behind enemy lines.

Without any means to expel these agents (pathogens) they (the viruses) are eventually incorporated into the cells of the body. This creates a profound confusion throughout the entire organism as to what is actually the organism (self), which is to be protected, and what is foreign (non-self), which is to be expelled.

At some point the immune system will begin to attack cells within the body to rid the organism of the foreign substance. This results in chronic auto-immune disease.

It is no mystery how much auto-immune disease there is in America today. The "people" who perpetrate the "immunization" crimes are well versed in psychological warfare.

Mass crimes are created under the altruistic phrase, "for the greater good." You who read this *Letter* are able to translate, "for the greater good" to always mean a transfer of more power to the corporate state.

They know that there are several years between the "immunization" shots and the appearance of auto-immune diseases. This is the perfect crime based on confusion of cause and effect.

Nazi Germany started mass compulsory immunization in 1940. The number of cases of diphtheria increased from 40,000 to 250,000 by 1945, virtually all among immunized children.

Bottom line for you: Mass inoculation and immunization is nothing more nor less than commerce via an alliance between big government and big pharmaceuticals. Further, this is an assault upon the people under a medical pretense.

Reference: *DPT; A Shot in the Dark,* by Harris Coulter. The literature states that homeopathic physicians can antidote vaccinations. See The Case Against Immunizations, by Richard Moskowitz M.D. Write: NCH, 801 North Fairfax St., Ste 306, Alexander, VA 22314 or call 1-703-548-7790.

Vaccinations: All About Money

Vaccinations are money to the drug producers as well as income to the doctors.

"Long ago, science warned physicians about the danger of post-vaccinal sleeping sickness poliomyelitis, syphilis, and other diseases. These diseases occur in children and adults alike following inoculations. Physicians know that a percentage of those they vaccinate or inoculate for diphtheria, scarlet fever, or measles, will die of shock, and that others will be projected into the Morphic night of sleeping sickness, or the disfiguring horrors of polio, while others will be stricken with rheumatic fever, arthritis, blindness, and suppurating rashes of all kinds.

Yet these results are justified by immunologists on the premise that the procedures are necessary to safeguard the population from epidemics. Their propaganda is that everything they do is "for the greater good." They overlook the fact that epidemics diminished as man purified his exterior environment. It is conceivable that the filth that once beset him in rags has come forth in a needle to destroy him." Quoted from the book *Bacteria, Inc.*, page 22.

Other countries have known for a hundred years that cimexlectularius (the bedbug) is a carrier of smallpox virus. Sanitation is the answer to smallpox, not vaccination.

When the bedbug was exposed as the carrier of smallpox, the manufacturing of serums had grown into a profitable industry and every doctor in the land was using vaccination as a lucrative part of his practice. The vaccination of every child before entering school had and has become an established practice.

Millions-upon-millions of vaccinations have netted trillions-of-dollars to the drug cartels and conventional medicine. Dr. Charles Campbell, bacteriologist, declared that smallpox is neither infectious nor contagious, and that vaccination does not prevent smallpox.

Italy has been without smallpox for 85 years without vaccinations. We take our newborn infants and inject into their little innocent bodies one devastating poison after another. The chemical balance of their body cells is disturbed, becoming polarized and defenseless against the external environment.

This is nothing less than assault upon these helpless infants in the name of preventing disease. No wonder Jesus wept!

Vaccinations are the big cause of immune malfunction. They have nothing to do with disease prevention and everything to do with commerce.

The germ theory of disease is the basis of modern medicine in the western world and it is a lie. Will anybody ever be held responsible for this crime?

References: *Bacteria, Inc.* This is a valuable book. This book is hard to find. I found only a couple on *Amazon.com* for sale (used). The Nutritional Research Foundation has agreed to reprint this book. Call them and ask for a copy and get their catalog. Call John Brady at 1-858-488-8932. *The Medical Mischief You Say, Degerminating the Germ Theory.* You have to search for this book. I only have one copy I've had for many,

many years. You might try a rare book search service. Bechamp or Pasteur, available at Health Research™ 1-888-844-2386.

Only Affected, Those Who Took Flu Shots

Dr. Eleanor McBean, who lived through the 1918 influenza epidemic, testified that the flu only hit people who had been vaccinated while the ones who refused the shots escaped the flu.

Dr. McBean's family refused the flu vaccinations, so they remained well. Many soldiers were vaccinated and many died or were seriously sick.

Flu shots and vaccines are such a huge profitable business each year that medical authorities tend toward statistical hallucinations in projecting large numbers of people who will be sick or die. Fear is used to make people conform.

The "flu salesmen" doctors and the Center for Disease Control (CDC) multiply the danger of viruses because without exaggerated stories flu vaccines just don't sell. People are slowly catching on. We have to remember that the American medical establishment is disease-oriented because there is not a penny to be made in prevention

If You Really Love Your Children

Protect your children from vaccines known to be worthless against disease, yet which can cause permanent illness and disability.

Dr. Sherri Tenpenny *(www.osteomed.com)* has dedicated her life's work to exposing the flu and vaccination crimes at the Center for Disease Control (CDC). She has investigated some crucial areas in the flu and vaccination crimes listed below:

■ How vaccines can cause illnesses including autoimmune diseases, allergies, and ear infections.

■ The very real link between vaccines and developmental and behavioral disorders in children.

■ How vaccines are mass produced and used and never proven safe.

■ All vaccines have contaminants.

■ So-called vaccine studies are seriously flawed.

Vaccines ARE Linked to Disease and Chronic Illness

The pharmaceutical giants profit immensely from vaccines and so they pour immense effort into suppressing information from the public. And the government is totally in active support of the pharmaceuticals.

This is a rich source of huge political donations. Dr. Sherri Tenpenny, (who probably knows more than any person in the United States about vaccines, the political motivation and money power behind them) says that the medical establishment is planning to make vaccinations universally mandatory. In other words, they intend to vaccinate every man, woman, and child in the United States.

This would be multiple vaccinations and it is called mass-forced medication. This should disturb anyone who is up to body temperature.

There are two kinds of vaccination enforcement:

1. The first kind is visible. If your children go to school without vaccination cards they are sent home. This intimidates parents into conformity. They don't know what to do but conform.

2. By far the most powerful is medical propaganda of the "benefits of vaccinations" until people clamor for it. This is a classic example of what benevolent totalitarianism is all about.

Forced vaccinations (inoculations) are a form of tyranny. It is bio-terrorism (to steal an establishment term). This is chemical warfare in a most disguised fashion.

Consent is manipulated into conformity. The people are persuaded with medical propaganda to consent and the next step is to manipulate them into conformity.

"Informed consent" is the method of benevolent totalitarianism. Once the masses are manipulated into conformity and they arrive at the animal farm in full mental submission, they themselves enforce conformity. This is the basic syndrome of George Orwell's *Animal Farm.*

Letting the inmates be in charge of the jail is the perfect crime. Another way to put it is that the inmates love their captivity and they love "big brother." They and "big brother" (the government) are of ONE MIND!

There is no dissent. All are ONE! This is the ultimate goal of the NEW WORLD ORDER. The spirit of subterfuge has become good and good has become evil.

From the *Book, Fats & Oils,* by Udo Erasmus: Earlier Maturity

Diets high in fats speed up the rate at which children mature. The average age of first menstruation in girls during the 17th century was 17 years old on a diet containing about 20 percent fat. The present average age of first menstruation is 13 years old on a diet containing 42 percent fat.

Faster Growth Rate: High-fat diets also increase the growth rate and adult body size of the people who consume these diets. This explains why the physical stature of human beings has increased over the last 100 years. It also explains why Japanese people living in Japan are shorter on average than Caucasians. Their diet is less than 15 percent fat compared to ours at more than 40 percent. When Japanese people come to North America and adopt the Western diet, their offspring become taller, and the same phenomenon holds true for other racial groups around the world.

Shorter Life Span: Earlier maturity and taller stature are balanced by shorter life span. People on a high-fat diet burn out quicker. The most recent theory to explain this is that free radicals produced from fats in the body cross-link the genetic material, cross-link proteins and produce toxic chemical compounds in the system, which hinder metabolism.

Other people suggest that aging is the result of the accumulation of breakdown products of metabolism which clog up the body chemistry, making enzymes less efficient and slow down the wheels of life until they stop. Still others talk about biological aging clocks, which run down like the spring in a watch. In practice, the more fanciful the theory, the less concrete evidence there is to sustain it. Most likely free radicals are involved. Metabolites are probably also involved. Either enhances the production of the other; and neither came first, just like the chicken and the egg.

Sugar: Besides fats, refined sugars (perhaps through their tendency to produce fats) also shorten life span. Therefore, exclusion of refined sugars from the diet will also slow aging and lengthen life span. Restriction of calories also slows aging. But nobody knows for sure what mechanisms in the body determine aging.

Diet Manipulation: If you want tall children who will live for a long time, feed them a high-fat diet until they are adults and then teach them to eat a low fat (and low sugar) diet for the rest of their lives. My mother says this is the way they used to feed their livestock to keep them healthy. The calves were fed high-fat foods, and when they were mature, they were switched to a low-fat (grass) diet. And that's apparently the way nature does it.

If you want children to stay children longer then keep them on a low-fat, low-sugar diet from the time you wean them off your breast. Dietary manipulation is common in nature and works for the bees. Bee larvae fed one kind of food become sterile workers who die after six weeks. Queen bee larvae, fed royal jelly, live up to eight very productive years. Dietary changes can also work for humans.

Population Control—Many Ways

1. Have a financial system (fiat) where both husband and wife are required to work.
2. Promote the cholesterol hoax, i.e. keep the "high risk of high cholesterol" before the people through the medical cartel. Get blood cholesterol below the levels needed to produce reproductive hormones.

3. Other side effects of low cholesterol such as cancer contribute to population decline.

4. Lower cholesterol increases heart disease and an increase in deaths from suicide and violence.

5. Very low cholesterol in children causes growth problems and many fail to reach sexual maturity. Investigators have cited the lack of protective nutrients found in animal fats as a factor against pounding cholesterol levels lower and lower. Cholesterol drugs do not reduce the risk of heart disease. Something worse is that CoQ10 is depleted as cholesterol is forced down. Cholesterol is vitally important, is responsible for building our cell membranes as well as many of our hormones.

Glandular Nutrition

For glandular nutrition, green foods and whole foods are best.

My family and I eat some meat, but mostly wild, unadulterated meats, grass fed beef, and fish. These meats contain no hormones, antibiotics, pesticide residues, or drugs.

Our ancestors consumed various organs and glands from their wild meat and did not eat the muscle meats such as steak. Today most people of the world do the opposite and favor the muscle meats.

Glandular therapy is the ingestion of organs and glands from fish and animals. This has been found to be good for health as well as preventing or treating specific ailments. The parts used are animal liver, kidneys, brain, heart, eyes, thyroid glands, thymus glands, and bone marrow.

This idea of "like heals like" means that the best food or treatment for a specific organ disease can be obtained by that particular counterpart of cow, sheep, or pig. There are still a few companies that produce these animal extracts using pure and clean organic meats.

Taste is not a problem because these animal organ extracts are in tablet form and any reference taste to animal protein is thoroughly masked. Overdosing is not a concern because hormones are not a part of the animal extracts. Animal glandulars are safe and effective.

Response can be measured and is not just subjective. It is a fact that whole-cell glandulars provide needed nutrition for specific tissues or organs.

Remember, like attracts like. It takes only a very small amount of glandular extract to have a significant effect on a large human organ.

Infections and the Common Cold

Normally we assume that if we have an infection we would know it.

Of course we would know it if the infection is on the outside of the body, but what about infections that are internal and not visible? Internal infections can be very subtle and extremely dangerous, leading to degenerative disease over time.

If the lymph glands get overloaded with toxemia, you could develop a blood cancer such as leukemia. An infection which is present but not recognized is called a subclinical infection. It could be under control for years and then manifest into serious illness.

Stagnant infections are many times associated with dental work, mercury amalgams, and root canal pockets. Many people are having their mercury amalgams removed and dental cavitations cleaned.

It is not a hard thing to do, but not all dentists are familiar with the problem of cavitations (pockets of infection.) They can only be seen with the use of special panoramic x-rays.

They cannot be detected with routine x-rays. Knowledgeable holistic doctors look for subclinical infections as a first cause of degenerative disease. If you have mercury amalgams and/or root canals, you may consider a panoramic x-ray just to be sure even if you have had your mercury amalgams removed.

Your teeth could be a problem. Better safe than sorry!

CHAPTER 11

Chemical Warfare

Hitler: "How Fortunate for Governments that the People They Administer Don't Think"

From military warfare to chemical warfare alias U.S. Pharmaceuticals: As the U.S. World War II machine raced across Europe to Germany, one of the hidden prizes was German chemical patents.

The German chemical cartel was critical to the German war machine. They were Bayer, Hoechst, Agfa, BASF, and some others. They developed a highly sophisticated synthetic chemical industry (cartel). The German chemical cartel invented and created chemical warfare. But, in between wars, profits have to be civilian sourced.

Now, change the name to U.S. pharmaceuticals and change the war against Germany to chemical warfare (prescriptions and medicines) against the American people. Any kind of warfare, whether military hostilities or esoteric warfare on civilian populations, always has attending propaganda.

How fortunate for pharmaceuticals that the American people have been sold on drugs as medicinal therapy.

The fact that historically whole foods are required for human healing, health, and longevity is a vague memory. Sickness and disease is a deficit of food nutrition, not a drug deficit as modern medicine implies. Think how foolish!! Eighty-five percent to 95 percent of all pharmaceuticals are created exclusively for profit. They have nothing at all to do with legitimate therapy.

Continued on page 129.

A Bob Livingston Perspective:

Health Revolution Stolen: A Great Conspiracy

The word "conspiracy" is very unpopular in our time. It's akin to sinful, dirty and against "public policy." It is certainly not politically correct. Professional and well-bred people just don't use it and they blank out any crude person who does as ignorant or paranoid. The very thought of conspiracy rattles polite society. I would expect that before the end of this generation that the word conspiracy will be left out of new editions of dictionaries.

Yet there are conspiracies founded on gross and mass deceptions. Most conspiracies are designed to gain either power or money or both.

One of the most clever deceptions and conspiracies is to capitalize on something that is already established or accepted, using its basic word phraseology and terminology. The good is corrupted and crowded out with a cheap substitute that produces huge profits.

In the early days of very small public acceptance of supplemental nutrition or vitamins, the Food and Drug Administration (FDA) sought a frontal attack against those pioneer creators and vendors of honest, natural nutrition.

Dr. Elmer M. Nelson, the second head of the FDA, tried to block health food processors from comparing the quality of their products with their synthetic counterparts. He said in testimony in federal court that: "It is wholly unscientific to state that a well-fed body is more able to resist disease than a less well-fed body. My overall opinion is that there hasn't been enough experimentation to prove dietary deficiencies make one more susceptible to disease." Only a government prostitute to big business would state such a blatant lie.

But in later years the synthetic vitamin industry shifted gears from a frontal attack to a more seductive deception. They realized that all they had to do was capitalize on the public's exploding desire for better health through better nutrition.

Indeed, they have capitalized on just two words. The result has chan- neled billions-of-dollars into the coffers of the big chemical manufacturers of synthetic vitamins. The words are NATURAL and ORGANIC.

The deception is based on letting these two words float around and appear on most vitamins sold when actually the FDA has not clearly defined these two words. It is left to the public to assume that these words imply that anything with the words "natural" or "organic" on them are directly from nature unadulterated.

This is not true at all as the FDA loosely defines natural and organic as anything that ultimately comes from nature. This could be anything under the sun, including chemicals. This of course means that synthetic vitamins made from coal tars, refined oils, and corn sugar may have the words natural or organic on them. This is an unconscionable criminal act, but it's "legal" and it is a ruse to put cheap imitations in the place of something truly unadulterated and direct from nature.

People who believe that they are buying supplemental health as "vitamins" don't know the seriousness of consuming chemicals under the name vitamin. The "vitamin" industry is now big business and big business is getting positioned to capture billions and billions of dollars. It is commercialism and health of the people be damned.

Millions more will die of degenerative disease as they gorge on synthetic vitamins. And note the hypocrisy whereas the FDA has muzzled health claims by nutritionists, the floodgates for the same claims by big business are now open.

The health revolution has been stolen.

Continued from page 127.

But constant propaganda creates a constant need and constant profits. How have millions of people become so docile and completely deceived by pharmaceutical drugs as healing agents? All the pharmaceuticals had to do to create a trillion dollar drug market is to teach the people that symptoms are causes.

This simple switch created a medical system of symptomology or a system of treating symptoms with drugs. Masking symptoms makes people feel better and it also confuses cause and effect. What a payoff! People never become aware of slow death as long as their symptoms are masked. Drugs are particularly suited for this.

A human body can deteriorate to death slowly and imperceptibly through acid saturation with synthetic foods and drugs. The system prevails because doctors themselves have been taught that drugs actually heal. They also confuse symptoms with cause. And the public pushes the system by clamoring for drugs.

The American people are victimized by a drug culture which they believe is medicine. Doctors are licensed by the State but *defacto* by the pharmaceuticals that can ruin them if they defy the drug system.

The new German Reich is not a military phenomenon. The U.S. pharmaceuticals have taught the world to exist on synthetic foods, synthetic drugs, and a political system to support our synthetic chemical industry (pharmaceuticals). There are no guns blazing and no blood in the streets, only friendly persuasion to take these chemicals (or these drugs) to rid yourself of symptoms.

Book References: *German Chemical Cartel Under Hitler* and *The Nazi War on Cancer.*

The Malicious Fraud of Smallpox and Other Vaccinations

Even if they worked and were without risk, vaccines only stimulate temporary immunity.

By trading lifelong immunity for temporary vaccine-induced immunity, people become vaccine dependent. The winners of repeated mandatory vaccinations are the pharmaceutical companies. The losers are the people, who are first put at risk as children for vaccine adverse events and then put at risk as adults for repeated vaccinations that have already failed.

The pharmaceuticals have discovered a money machine in mass vaccinations. But they need and have to have your body for the pretense.

The development of asthma and diabetes in children has increased substantially in the last three decades, coinciding with the significant increase in childhood immunizations.

Public awareness has been manipulated. Why does no one

question the authority of injecting agents of unknown toxicity into their body.

Unbelievably, the general public is satisfied with the disinformation provided by the government. Unfortunately, now is the wrong time for apathy.

We are on the verge of a vaccine mania, and by the time our wakeup call comes it just may be too late. The worldwide market for human vaccine is now over $10 billion with the underlying purpose cloaked by the guise of protecting public health.

The act of forcing people through intimidation and deception into dangerous medications is terrorism of the most malicious sort. This act by public authority constitutes assault, violating civil and human rights under national and international law. There can be no "greater good" in this act of war against the American people.

Got Milk? The Moustache Conspiracy

Everywhere you look is a huge signboard touting the drinking of milk. It's been going on for years. Can you imagine the budget for this promotion? Well, what is this sinister conspiracy?

Just like the synthetic (chemical) vitamin conspiracy, the milk conspiracy has seized upon a basic American response to the word milk. Milk historically has been a staple for the American diet.

The problem is that there is no milk for the American consumer. Raw wholesome milk was phased out 50 years ago under the pretense of health. Live, whole, fresh milk has been replaced with pasteurized and later homogenized "milk." This product of commerce has absolutely no similarity to whole cow's milk except both are white.

Commercial milk is dead. All the enzymes and nutrition have been killed with heat. It won't sour like whole milk; it rots because it is dead. It is a negative food and it's dangerous. Most can't digest it.

But the point here is that the American people think that milk is milk just like they think that vitamins are vitamins.

Do you know that this is chemical warfare using commercial foods as chemicals? We assume that chemical warfare like the recent anthrax attacks kills very quickly. But chemical warfare is just as deadly and lethal if we accumulate chemicals in our bodies over time. Degenerative disease may not show up for years but it eventually will.

In fact all commercial foods, devoid of nutrition, are a form of chemical warfare against the population. Slow starvation with a full belly.

Deadly Chlorine in Your Drinking Water and Your Bath Water

Many people have become alerted to the serious danger of chlorine in their drinking water but almost nobody seems to be concerned about chlorine in their bath water. Water is chlorinated all over America except for only a few small towns. When taking a bath, you absorb far more chlorine than when you are drinking water. Your whole body soaks up the toxic chlorine and you breathe the gas chloroform.

Chlorine causes heart attacks, according to Dr. Joseph Price in his book, *Coronaries, Cholesterol, and Chlorine.* The chlorine in water inhibits iodine uptake of the thyroid.

Chlorine is an allergen that causes depression, according to Dr. Hulda Clark.

Chlorinated shower water puts a lot of chlorine (chloroform) into the air which is distributed throughout the house. Chloroform is one of the trihalomethane group (THMs) which is formed when chlorine reacts with other harmless organic substances already present in the water to form THMs. They are found in the water of over 100 million Americans.

Researchers have found that trihalomethanes and disinfection by-products may be responsible for over 10,000 rectal and bladder cancers per year.

Death by Prescription Drugs

The dictionary term is "iatrogenic death." This means death induced in a patient by a physician's activity, manner or therapy, according to the *American Heritage Dictionary*. Our society has many contradictions and quirks, but they don't seem to bother us. The politicians want gun confiscation while they purposely overlook 250,000 deaths a year at the hands of the medical establishment's drug deaths. All the wars in history and all the gun deaths are no match for drug deaths.

And I don't mean illegal drugs. I mean prescription drugs. If we were sane, we would say this is nothing but mass murder. It makes gun control the biggest hypocrisy on earth. In fact, victims of prescription drugs commit many serious crimes. Prescription drugs can turn people into monsters.

If people would read the inserts of the everyday drugs that they are taking, they would run from doctors. These inserts tell you the high risk, but who reads anymore?

"Health Care"—a Cover for Euthanasia

Murder is acceptable if it can be made benevolent, passed off as "health care." We have long advocated that vaccines are an assault upon the people under the pretense of health care. It is forced medication through persuasion.

"Health care" in America is a system of killing off weak infants and aging adults. This is not largely suspected because of the disassociation of cause and effect. Nobody even suspects. The mode is vaccinations and inoculations.

If there is a very rare protest, the "authorities" just say that an occasional death is unavoidable and is for the "greater good." That term the "greater good" is statist philosophy that the people are cattle and some have to be sacrificed.

But mass inoculations kill en masse. It's silent murder as "health care."

This killing system is being perfected and fine-tuned without so much as a ripple of protest. Would you say the "perfect crime?" Incredible? Yes, the more incredible, the more perfect the crime. Examples:

1. Autistic children because of mercury vaccines.

2. AIDS epidemic in Africa associated with the use of SI— Simian Immunodeficiency Virus. (Monkey-human genetic virus.)

3. Two experimental AIDS vaccines have just been foisted on citizens of Thailand with a propaganda appeal for patriotism and a plea for people to think of "the greater good." The drug company goal is to force mandatory AIDs vaccinations.

4. Urine samples from hundreds of French children have yielded evidence for a link between autism and exposure to heavy metals.

5. Anthrax vaccines were forced on U.S. soldiers that proved unsafe and unnecessary. The deaths were admitted along with a wide-range of autoimmune disorders. Government involved in cover-up.

6. A new vaccine to "protect" against a common sexually transmitted disease in children age eight to 12. This is a vaccine against immoral behavior. What next?

7. The bird flu hype has been fanned by public health officials using fear to keep the public scared.

Vaccines kill natural immunity. Natural exposure to "germs" in childhood can lead to natural immunity and long-term health. Health authorities kill infectious microorganisms with the mass use of multiple vaccines.

So-called "public health" is a cover for mass medication and selective killing, at first "voluntary" and then mandatory.

We recommend you watch the movie *Soylent Green* with Charlton Heston and Edwin G. Robinson. Also, stay in touch with National Vaccine Information Center online at *www.nvic.org*.

You can also check out the DVD *"FOWL! What They're Not Telling You About the Avian Flu,"* $9.99 from *www.herballure.com* or 1-800-358-4278.

The Future of Nutritional Freedom

Frankly, I do not expect nutritional freedom to last in the United States, simply because natural remedies are expanding in the public conscious while conventional medicine is beginning to smell.

When the public begins to buy health remedies with their own money outside the medical monopoly, they are taking responsibility for their own health, something the pharmaceutical cartel absolutely does not want. Hence, expect a more sophisticated and determined effort to transfer natural health alternatives under licensed medical control as it already is in Europe.

Indeed, the pharmaceuticals have gone a long way to destroy alternatives with the mass production of synthetics as substitutes for naturals. The public is oblivious to this chicanery, proving that anything can be destroyed by manipulation and without force.

What About Prescription Drugs?

Your doctor or urologist has many FDA approved drugs to treat an enlarged prostate gland and its symptoms, but like surgery, they too can have undesirable and dangerous side effects.

Pharmaceutical companies do not offer any solutions. They cannot patent herbal extracts and charge the $5 or more a tablet they do for highly dangerous and ineffective treatments like Proscar®.

The answer is simply greed and indifference to your health. Has your doctor told you of the side effects of frequently prescribed drugs like Proscar®, Hytrin®, and Flomax®?

Proscar® has been shown to be moderately successful in reducing prostate size in some men and in addressing some of the urinary symptoms associated with BPH. However, it can take as long as six months before it shows results, and the drug has negative side effects, including a substantial increase in prostate cancer risk.

In fact, men who take this drug have their prostate cancer risk increased 300 percent, according to a 1999 clinical study conducted by the prestigious Norris Cancer Institute of the

University of Southern California (USC).

It also has the potential to decrease libido, cause premature ejaculation, and impotence. It can even cause birth defects in pregnant women who come in contact with the drug or possibly even with the sperm of a man who has taken Proscar®. It can also artificially lower a man's PSA levels by as much as 60 percent. This is very important to note, because it can interfere with the results of a PSA test in detecting prostate cancer.

Another category of drugs, called alpha-blockers, is prescribed for symptoms of BPH. They act by relaxing the smooth muscle of the prostate gland and neck of the bladder to improve urine flow.

One such drug, terazosin, is marketed under the name Hytrin®. Unfortunately, alpha-blockers can also have undesirable side effects, including headaches, fatigue, nasal congestion, dizziness, and even sudden loss of consciousness.

What is more important than these potentially dangerous side-effects is that these alpha-blockers do nothing but temporarily relieve BPH symptoms. You cannot get well by treating symptoms!

Aspartame: Sweet Poison

"The thing that bugs me is that the people think the FDA is protecting them — it isn't. What the FDA is doing and what the public thinks it's doing are as different as night and day."
—Dr. Herbert L. Ley, former FDA commissioner (1969)

Aspartame (NutraSweet®) was approved as a food additive by the FDA. More than 100 million persons in the United States, often in large amounts, are currently consuming Aspartame products. It is fast being put in every food and drink that requires sweetener.

Yet, it is well known that Aspartame causes severe headaches, seizures (convulsions), impairment of vision, dizziness, pain in the eyes, ears, face, neck and chest, rashes, extreme fatigue, depression, changes of personality, confusion, and memory loss.

Aspartame containing products and NutraSweet® itself is the

subject of the largest advertising campaign ever based on a product ingredient. One of its ingredients is methanol, which is synonymous with wood alcohol, a deadly poison even when consumed in relatively modest amounts.

Source: *Aspartame NutraSweet®, Is It Safe?* by Dr. H.J. Roberts, M.D.

Sugar and Glycemic Response

Eating fat does not make you fat. Sugar makes fat. Fat does not raise cholesterol or triglycerides. Sugar raises cholesterol and triglycerides.

Doctors are ignorant on this. All they know is a "low-fat diet." This is wrong and dangerous. The lower our sugar consumption, the more fat melts away.

Be advised that sugar in a food product can appear as carbo-hydrates, maltodextrins, glucose polymers, and under many other deceptive names. It's the glycemic index that gets us regardless of the name.

Glycemic Response: The blood sugar and insulin-stimulating properties of a sugar or sweetener can be defined by its glycemic response. A high glycemic sugar or sweetener will overly elevate blood sugar and insulin levels. A low glycemic sugar or sweetener does not overly elevate blood sugar and insulin levels.

Fat-Storing Response: The fat-storing effects of a sugar or sweetener can be defined by its high fat storage (HFS) properties defined as its ability to stimulate lipoprotein (LPL) and other fat-stimulating enzymes and proteins.

Reduced-caloric sweeteners—very low or no glycemic response—are: Matitol, sorbitol, isomalt, xylitol, HSH, erythritol, mannitol, Lo Han, and lactitol.

CHAPTER 12

Diabetes Prevention

Natural, Healthy Sweetness: Peruvian Stevia

Sugar and sweeteners of all types, except natural honey and natural Peruvian stevia, are highly toxic chemicals. The sugar deception is a great undisclosed health addiction that has wrecked the health of multimillions.

All disease directly relates to sugar consumption: This includes white and brown sugar and all the synthetic chemical sugars.

Sugar and especially synthetic chemical sweeteners are basic ingredients used by all commercial food processors. Some are more toxic than others, but all can cause multiple diseases from convulsions to diabetes. All accumulate as acid poisons in the human body.

Stevia: (*Stevia rebaudiana* from Peru) is a natural herb sweetener that is up to 300 times sweeter than sugar. South Americans have used this totally non-caloric sweet herb for more than 1,500 years. It is widely used all over the world, but as you would guess, it cannot be sold as a sweetener in the United States because of lobbyists for the artificial sweetener cartel and the FDA. It can be purchased only as a dietary supplement.

"In addition to its natural, powerfully sweet taste, (you only use a very mild, light dusting) research shows that stevia actually regulates blood sugar and reduces high blood pressure. It's an extremely effective aid in weight loss and weight management because it contains no calories. It also reduces your desire for alcohol and tobacco use," according to James Balch, M.D., in his excellent newsletter *Prescriptions for Healthy Living.*

Stevia has no glycemic index which means that it does not affect insulin in any negative way. This is good news to a nation of diabetics. It's a miracle as a food supplement for everybody.

Research in Japan has found Stevia to be perfectly safe to be used in any food recipe, chewing gum, or mouthwash. It is used on cereals, herb teas, coffee, and anything else that you desire.

Stevia is high in chromium (which helps to stabilize blood sugar), manganese, potassium, selenium, silicon, sodium, and vitamin A. It also contains iron, niacin, phosphorus, riboflavin, thiamine, vitamin C, and zinc.

Stevia also inhibits the growth of gum disease bacteria and tooth decay and in many countries it is used in oral hygiene products. You can make your own concentrated Stevia liquid by diluting Stevia powder with water. Simply swish in your mouth and swallow. This ability of Stevia to destroy infectious organisms may help explain why Stevia users report fewer colds and flu.

Less known but no less remarkable is the ability of water-based Stevia concentrates to help heal numerous skin problems, including acne, seborrhea (discharge of sebaceous matter on the head causing dry scales or dandruff), dermatitis, and eczema.

It also has been observed that placing it on cuts and wounds brings more rapid healing without scarring. It may cause a severe stinging for several seconds, but is followed by a significant lowering of pain. Physicians have reported using Stevia concentrate to heal psoriasis and burns, while others have reported that it is extremely helpful in healing various lip sores.

Switching to Stevia concentrate for all your sweet needs can be an extremely important step in restoring your health and in reversing the aging process.

Heartburn, Antacids, and Diabetes

Is the antacid causing parasites and diabetes?

Advertising sells us billions of dollars worth of Tums®, Rolaids®, Tagamet®, Zantac®, Digel®, etc. Americans are sold massive amounts of antacids believing that their stomach acids (acid indigestion) are causing heartburn.

Actually, the reverse is true. It is a deficiency of hydrochloric acid (HCl) that causes heartburn.

What is the effect of the antacids? They destroy the body's attempt to break down proteins, setting up a bowel toxic condition and destroying the all-important intrinsic factor needed to secrete vitamin B12.

The normal stomach should be very acidic with a pH as low as 2. If we make our pH too alkaline with antacids, we can cause the putrefaction of food complicating other biological functions and creating an environment for intestinal parasites. Stomach acid at the proper pH destroys parasite eggs.

Now comes a relationship of intestinal parasites to diabetes. The pancreas produces protein-digesting enzymes, but parasites are much harder for the pancreas to digest.

Remember, the parasites should have been killed in the stomach with normal hydrochloric acid before they get into the body. The effect is that the pancreas exhausts itself trying to produce enough enzymes to destroy the parasites.

This general wearing down of the pancreas wears down the Islets of Langerhans and of course their ability to produce insulin, causing diabetes. So antacids destroy natural stomach acids creating an environment for parasites, leading to diabetes.

If you have gastritis, with heartburn-like symptoms, barley grass juice is probably the best thing that you could take for permanent relief. Then you wouldn't need to reach for the antacids.

Magnesium Deficiency Linked to Diabetes

A major disease in which magnesium deficiency is rampant is diabetes. In fact, in diabetes, extreme magnesium loss is common.

The magnesium factor is critical, but little known. The association between magnesium deficiency and diabetes is well established. There is a high correlation between diabetes and heart disease, as both are directly related to intracellular magnesium levels.

Magnesium is an important co-factor in the production of insulin by the pancreas. Normal total body magnesium is essential for glucose metabolism. Thus, the rampant magnesium deficiency in our society may be a contributing cause of diabetes.

Glucose Can Cause Diabetes

Glucose causes diabetes when it is fed to test animals. No amount of natural sugar will do this. Synthetic glucose goes through the intestinal walls too quickly, putting a tremendous load on the pancreas, causing diabetes.

The wide use of synthetic sugars is nothing but an attempt by the commercial food industry to make something out of nothing. They are doing it and have been for years. This practice is serious because it blocks calcium assimilation.

Special interests would never allow a synthetic sugar cause and effect research to be published. They may find that diabetes and cancer are caused by synthetic sugars. The merchants of death don't care about anything but profits.

Wine for Diabetics

Sounds awful, but it does help. Be sure to monitor your blood sugar.

Diabetes causes vascular disease and almost certainly heart disease. The French have proved that daily moderate wine consumption lowers their national heart attack rate significantly.

In fact, a University of Wisconsin study which compared people who never drink with people who do take one or more drinks daily found that the latter cut the drinkers' risk of fatal heart attack by 79 percent. That's a whopper of a difference.

Remember moderation and keep check on your blood sugar. Adjust your wine intake accordingly.

A Few Facts About Sugar

The average American consumes approximately 32 teaspoons of sugar each day.

Obviously, since that's the average, many consume much, much more than 32 teaspoons each day. After all, one 12-ounce can of soda contains approximately nine teaspoons of sugar.

If you were to ingest the equivalent of 32 teaspoons of sugar from a natural source such as sugar cane, you would have to chew over 90 feet of sugar cane each day. Sugar consumption has been associated with heart disease, dental caries, diabetes, acne, gallbladder disease, indigestion, and much more.

One critical factor about sugar consumption has to do with disease resistance. White blood cells increase in number in the bloodstream when the body has a bacterial infection. These cells destroy bacteria. They are the body's soldiers.

However, when the blood sugar level goes up, these cells get sluggish and cannot destroy as many bacteria. Take a look at the following chart which shows how sugar intake affects the ability of while blood cells to destroy bacteria:

Amount of Sugar Eaten	No. of Bacteria Destroyed by WBC	% Decrease in Ability to destroy Bacteria
0 teaspoons	14	0%
6 teaspoons	10	25%
12 teaspoons	5.5	60%
18 teaspoons	2	85%
24 teaspoons	1	92%

CHAPTER 13

Weight Loss

Weight Loss Sleeper

No matter what you do, as long as you're taking in a single milligram of caffeine in a day, you're never going to lose an ounce. Caffeine stimulates your adrenal glands.

So to lose weight we have to turn down the adrenal glands and turn up the thyroid. It's relatively easy to turn down the adrenal glands.

All we have to do is eat licorice root. Licorice root will strengthen the adrenals and cause them to work only when they should.

The Truth About Aspirin: No Help for Weight Loss

It has become "common knowledge" that "an aspirin a day" can benefit heart health by thinning the blood, preventing blood vessel plaque build-up, and thus improving circulation. In some circles it is also said that aspirin improves metabolism, thus leading to weight loss.

Regarding the latter, Dr. Tracy Horton of the Center for Human Nutrition at the University of Colorado in Denver and Dr. Catherine A. Geissler of the Department of Nutrition and Dietetics at King's College of the University of London conducted a study that states: "Aspirin does not further potentiate the acute thermic effect found in higher metabolism rates."

In other words, aspirin does not help the body burn calories.

Drink Water to Lose Weight

If our bodies are mostly water, common sense tells us that we need to consume a lot of water. If fact, we are 80 percent to 90 percent water.

Really, the great need for more water consumption is not generally known. If the general population awakens to this, the FDA will have to find a way to make water a prescription drug. Probably, the psychological reason that people are not conscious of the serious need for pure drinking and bath water for health is that it's too simple and too cheap.

Somehow simplicity destroys credibility and value to Americans. It really costs them.

Water above all flushes out the toxins in our bodies. Accumulation of toxins is the ultimate cause of death. Also, water aids in digestion and regulates your body temperature like the radiator in your car. Imagine running your car without water like you do your body.

Water aids weight loss, flushes your cells, and supports your immune function in total. Be sure to drink pure water. Drink distilled water. It gives the added benefit of flushing debris.

Modern America:
Fat, Overweight, and Obese

From 14 percent overweight in 1994 to 33 percent in 2008. What's happening? We know for sure that we have an epidemic and a crisis.

Billions-of-dollars of diet plans are being touted to the American people, most of them worthless with false hope. I have bought a few myself. This is a disgrace and there is little promise of help.

Like everything else in America, the fat epidemic is going from bad to worse. So goes the American diet—so goes obesity.

Most of the American diet is bad but there is one thing in particular that is turning the whole population into diabetics. It's fructose corn syrup.

The food cartel is using millions of tons of this non-food as a cheap filler. This is more dangerous to the American people than a standing army.

Obesity is far more serious than most of us can imagine. It is inconvenient to say the least. It is deadly to say the most.

My recent study on this subject has me in shock. Obesity and overweight is far, far more serious than I suspected. There is a definite connection between getting sick and gaining weight. Let's talk about it.

If we could feel the silent sickness that goes along with the weight gain, most of us would be afraid to death to gain an ounce. Now that we are already fat, what's the story?

I hope that I can shock you with the following statement: **According to my study since I last wrote to you, obesity and overweight is related to and causative of every illness documented, including the degenerative diseases of cancer and heart disease!**

Overweight and fat, besides disrupting the immune system, creates chronic and silent inflammation which sets in motion a chain of biochemical events that results in a hormonal imbalance called leptin or insulin resistance, a condition that makes it nearly impossible to maintain a healthy weight.

As most believe, fat is not an inert storehouse of calories. It is an active organ that produces its own hormones. In fact, fat regulates itself.

When we gain weight, our fat produces the hormone leptin which is supposed to speed up our metabolism and suppress our appetite, causing weight to remain stable. Research has shown that extra weight or fat is not just an extra load to carry. As stated above, it is another of the body's internal organs. Moreover, it is an endocrine organ—the only organ with an almost unlimited ability to increase in size.

This is one organ that we don't want. And after it appears this is a definite signal that we already have a chemical imbalance and a high probability of low-grade whole-body inflammation that may have already triggered a disease process.

If we don't feel anything or see evidence of a medical problem, the extra weight that we carry is not yet symptomatic of disease. But obesity upsets our chemical balance by tipping the scale toward very destructive inflammation.

This is not visible inflammation as seen with a surface injury. This is inflammation at the cellular level, completely hidden.

We can detect evidence of the disease process caused by this obese condition. One way is if we have an apple shape and lower abdominal fat, we are almost certain of what we call metabolic syndrome or insulin resistance.

Abdominal obesity is generally considered to be a waist circumference, as measured around the middle, of greater than 40 inches for men and 35 inches for women.

Another indicator of metabolic syndrome or insulin resistance is the C-reactive protein blood test. This test has become very well known as an inflammatory marker. Elevated C-reactive proteins is an almost certain indicator of cardiovascular risk, high cholesterol, high blood pressure, maybe diabetes, colorectal and breast cancer, age-related cognitive decline, and premature death.

In fact, aging is now considered to be a process of ongoing inflammation. All this comes out of being obese or fat.

Few people are aware of all the complications of weight gain, especially abdominal weight gain.

Fat by itself produces inflammation, but diet is also a huge factor. **The proper diet can reverse obesity and inflammation.** As I will tell you below, it is a simple diet but a very rewarding one.

Unfortunately most American diets are rich in inflammatory ingredients which are red meat, white flour, sugar, and hydrogenated or transfats such as French fries.

On the other hand, berries and cherries, walnuts and almonds, cabbage, broccoli, garlic, and fish are super foods that will restore health.

This is not complicated, and these are very delicious healthy foods.

Bad food got us into this very critical inflammatory syndrome. Good food will get us out.

The simplicity of the causes of obesity does not seem to match the critical illnesses that result.

It all points to how devastating the wrong food is for health. It is as if to say, and many writers do, that food is more powerful than drugs.

What is the nitty-gritty cause of this silent inflammation and the destruction to our health that it brings? Yes, I said that it is bad food, but let's be more specific. **It is actually unbalanced fatty acids, mainly Omega-3s and Omega-6s.**

Simply stated, there are some Omega-3 foods and there are some Omega-6 foods.

The American diet is predominantly Omega-6s and Omega-6s are way out of balance with Omega- 3s.This causes silent inflammation, obesity, serious and terminal diseases, and illness.

The action to take is to rebalance our Omega-3s with our Omega-6s with diet. First, we must learn what Omega-3s and Omega-6s are so that we can reduce our Omega-6s and raise our Omega-3s. Actually it may be mostly reducing our Omega-6s. An ideal ratio would be three Omega-3s to five Omega-6s. Your body will tell you.

For more exciting details read our references: *The Fat Resistance Diet* by Dr. Leo Galland, *Win The War Within* by Floyd H. Chilton, Ph.D. and *The Anti Inflammation Zone* by Barry Sears, Ph.D.

Food for Those Overweight!

From Dr. Royal Lee: "Eat potatoes instead of bread" is good advice for the overweight who are constantly engaged in the battle of the calories.

Pound for pound, potatoes furnish about one-third fewer

calories than bread—so we may eat three times as much on a
caloric basis. (There are about 100 calories per medium-sized
raw potato, which is much less than a serving of spaghetti, pie,
or cake.) In addition, its superior digestibility and food value
as a source of protein, vitamins, and minerals make it ideal for
reducing the caloric intake without sacrifice of many essential
food factors.

According to Dr. Lee the dilemma—now a crisis—of obesity
is processed foods. Processed foods are foods we buy prepared
and foods that we cook. These are actually incomplete foods
because most of what we eat are dead foods that cannot support
life in a healthy state.

Virtually the only reliable source of complete food complexes
today is found in raw foods. Raw apples, potatoes, vegetables,
fruits, raw meats, eggs, unpasteurized raw milk, cream, and
butter—all are foods which, under present-day circumstances,
are as complete as it is possible to obtain. If obesity were attacked
with raw foods, not only would the problem be obliterated,
but the condition of our nation would improve to the point
where we, instead of being the sickest nation on earth, would
be the healthiest.

Obesity is a disease of civilization, or better stated,
un-civilization. It is the primitive races that are civilized.
They eat whole raw foods and they do not have obesity,
cancer, diabetes, hardening of the arteries, tooth decay, etc.

And they don't have a medical establishment and an FDA to
parasite on them. In the so-called civilized world the system
debauches our health and then the "medical establishment"
profits from sickness.

Eat Fat, Lose Weight

The anti-fat mongers are out in full force and they have been
for years—long enough that most people are deceived. Go in any
supermarket and pick up most any food product and it will say
"low fat" or "no fat."

Well, there are two kinds of fats. One is good and one is bad, but the good fats have been thrown out with the bad. Good fats are critically important to human health. If you can change your mind about good fats you can return to health and lose all the excess weight you want.

Your new energy and new health will be unbelievable.

The Dangers of Transfats: Manufactured foods such as baked goods, some frozen foods, margarine, potato chips, fast food fries, and countless transfats which are produced artificially by bombarding poly unsaturated oils with hydrogen, a process called "partial hydrogenation" that you see so much on manufactured food products. So the transfats have a longer shelf life but shorten your life in a very serious way.

The transfats or altered fats increase the risk of heart disease and greatly promote weight gain while compromising many bodily functions including insulin metabolism, a key factor in weight gain, and metabolic syndrome.

Healthy Fats: Healthy fats are not altered or processed with high heat. Good fats include Omega-3 fatty acids and are found in cod-liver oil, egg yolks, and flax oil. Medium-chain saturated fats are found in coconut oil, palm kernel oil, and real unprocessed butter. Long-chain saturated fats are found mostly in meat and dairy products.

All these fats will help you lose weight, increase your energy, boost your immunity to illness, and optimize your digestion.

Yes, I am telling you that raw butter, raw cream, egg yolks, meat fats, and all coconut products restore your health and cause you to lose weight. And no, it will not offend your blood lipids (fats). They will miraculously return to normal without drugs. You will have new and lasting energy and you will never be hungry again.

And let coconut oil lead the way to your new-slim world.

Why coconut oil? Because it is easy to digest and because most of the fatty acids it contains don't require bile for digestion. So the body turns these fatty acids directly into energy, making it terrific for losing weight. Try adding two tablespoons a day to your diet.

Overweight and obesity is a severe reaction from excess calories with a deficiency of nutrition. If nutritional balance is not restored, weight will never be normalized. Nutritional deficits impair metabolism. Junk food carbohydrates are converted to fat and stored in fat cells. All processed or commercial foods are devitalized and will induce weight gain.

When we eat refined carbohydrates such as refined sugars (including all synthetic or chemical sweeteners, except Stevia) and their products: Candy, cake, pie, ice cream, soda drinks, cookies, etc. along with refined flours and white flour, we are self destructing. Add to this corn syrup, high fructose corn syrup, sucrose, glucose, fructose, dextrose, sorbitol, margarine, hydrogenated shortenings, crackers, potato chips, commercially fried foods, French fries, pasteurized milk, cooking vegetable oils, etc., etc. All processed foods such as those listed above are made with altered or transfats.

Oh yes, there is plenty to eat such as fresh raw nuts and seeds, fresh raw fruits and vegetables organically grown when possible, lightly cooked or steamed vegetables and legumes. Also unprocessed meats (wild if possible), fish, poultry, yard eggs (if possible), raw milk and raw milk products such as cheese and real butter, unrefined oils like coconut, olive oil, or any other unheated oils and natural sea salt.

Of course these lists are far from complete. We have to read labels constantly.

I tell you frankly, most people don't have a chance to lose excess fat because they are addicted to sugar in all forms along with trans-fats.

The commercial food processors can create taste and addiction out of nonfoods. But the body cannot make health out of nothing. The whole population is trying to do it.

The commercial food processors are castrating the whole nation. Studies unequivocally show that the male sperm count is consistently going down, and has for 75 years. This is silent population control most dear to the heart of the Malthusians. And just think how a rising tide of sick people is more fodder for the medical cartel. And our children start their heart disease when they are born.

The only permanent weight loss system that will restore health is a high protein, high-fat diet such as outlined by Dr. Robert Atkins in *New Diet Revolution;* Dr. Mary Enig and Sally Fallon's *Eat Fat, Lose Fat;* and *The Protein Power Lifeplan* by Michael R. Eades M.D. and Mary Dan Eades, M.D.

One never gets commitment by just thinking that he wants to lose weight. It's a study in itself but worth it many times over.

Overweight people, and that's 40 percent of us, are sick people headed for more chronic sickness and disease and early death.

How the biochemistry of *Eat Fat, Lose Fat* works: It's the healthiest way of life and it is not a calorie thing. Eat all you desire of the right foods just like our ancestors before the modern fat age began.

As we get older our bodies may have a set point. Our weight may remain constant and all seems well, but we are gaining body fat yet maintaining body weight. As we age, our body composition changes. We lose muscle mass and gain body fat. We want to reverse this for appearance and equally for health. It's harder as we get older but more than worth the effort. It's not a big deal at all once we get in the habit. What if it extends quality life a few years?

Our main concern is to lose fat not weight, and this is the order in which it happens on the high fat, high protein diet.

Excess fat is far, far more of a concern than excess body weight in the form of lean body mass or more muscle weight. Muscle weighs more than fat. There is discouragement at first until one understands the ratio of lean muscle to fat. Don't look at the numbers on the scales but watch your shape change and reapportion for excitement. Inches will be lost, clothes will be looser and flab will disappear. Weight will come off!

It is important to understand that as you change on the outside with high fat and high protein, you are changing on the inside. All factors will be reversed toward health and many drugs will no longer be needed. Your blood pressure, your lipid profile, your insulin balance and all factors will be gradually reversed toward normal. This is absolute proof of high fat, high protein, no matter what people believe!

Fat and protein satiates (satisfies) and does away with carbohydrate craving and accelerates the burning of stored fat.

When we come to really believe that sugar in all its forms is a metabolic poison, we will gladly and excitedly switch to high protein and high fat.

Those who are serious will read and study Dr. Atkins' *New Diet Revolution* and/or Dr. Mary Enig and Sally Fallon's book *Eat Fat, Lose Fat.*

I am excited and grateful.

CHAPTER 14

Healthy Alternatives

Water Cure... for Free!

According to F. Batmanghelidj, M.D., author of *Your Body's Many Cries For Water,* **70 percent of the medical mafia would collapse if everyone would drink at least eight glasses of water per day and take a total of 1/4 teaspoon of sea salt per quart of water taken throughout the day. This comes as close to being a silver bullet as you are ever going to find.**

Of course you likely won't see immediate results, but please give it an honest try. Do it as a new way of life. It's a new paradigm that is going to change the health of the world.

Sure, you will need your food supplements with the water, but you won't need nearly as many doctors. You should see quick results.

If you have gastritis (no matter how bad) try the water cure, eight to 10 glasses of water per day with 1/4 teaspoon of sea salt per quart of water. One of our associates had serious gastritis for 30 years and 90 percent of it was gone within 24 hours. Now he is almost totally recovered.

The human body is an acid-consuming, acid-producing, and acid-eliminating organism. Acidosis symptoms imply dehydration.

Dr. Batmanghelidj says that most illnesses are not illness at all but only symptoms of dehydration. He says that we are not sick, we are thirsty.

Asthma? Do you know anyone with asthma? Try the water cure! It works and it's FREE!

It is our strong belief that in time the very simple and cost-less water cure will undermine and collapse the great medical conspiracy.

Drink More Water!

Because:

- 75 percent of Americans are chronically dehydrated.
- In 35 percent of Americans, the thirst mechanism is so weak that it is often mistaken for hunger. Most of the time when we are eating, we should be drinking water—even more so as we get older.
- Even mild dehydration will slow down one's metabolism as much as 3 percent.
- One glass of water shuts down hunger pains.
  Lack of water is the No. 1 trigger of daytime fatigue.
- Research indicates that eight to 10 glasses of water a day can significantly ease back and joint pain for up to 80 percent of sufferers.
- Eight to 10 glasses of water a day will reduce the risk of colon cancer, breast cancer, and bladder cancer.

Your "Clean" Bottled Water?

Aquafina® maker Pepsi® says that the leading bottled water brand comes from the same source as tap water.

Soon labels will include the words "Public Water Source" instead of "P.W.S." Pepsi's® Aquafina® and Coca-Cola® Company's Dasani® are both made from purified water sourced from public reservoirs, as opposed to Danone's®, Evian® or Nestle's® Poland Spring®, so-called "spring waters," shipped from specific locations the companies say have notably clean water.

"Concerns about the bottled-water industry, and increasing corporate control of water, are growing across the country," said Gigi Kellett, director of the "Think Outside the Bottle" campaign, which aims to encourage people to drink tap water.

San Francisco's mayor banned city employees from using city funds to buy bottled water when tap water is available. Ann Arbor, Michigan, passed a resolution banning commercially bottled water at city events, and Salt Lake City, Utah asked department heads to eliminate bottled water.

Critics charge the bottled water industry adds plastic to landfills, uses too much energy by producing and shipping bottles across the world, and undermines confidence in the safety and cleanliness of public water supplies. And while all this goes on, much of the world's population is without access to clean water.

Magnesium Deficiency

Magnesium deficiency is one of the major contributors to cardiac arrhythmia, angina, high cholesterol, high blood pressure, and sudden death from heart attack.

There is no fear of overload of magnesium in the diet. Any excess is excreted harmlessly. Magnesium can bring on diarrhea in some people the first few days, but it does not last long.

A deficiency of magnesium is dangerous for the nervous system, heart, and kidneys. Unfortunately, almost everyone is low in magnesium. Ultimate Calcium™ from Health Resources™ contains 40 percent magnesium.

Natural Bug Repellent

Essential oils are effective natural bug repellants.

While DEET is effective, studies show that essential oils work very well when it comes to deterring bugs. A 2001 Iowa State University study found that catnip essential oil is 10 times more effective at repelling mosquitoes than DEET.

Additionally, the CDC has given a nod to the active ingredient in oil of lemon eucalyptus as one of just three products recommended against West Nile virus. The other two approved by the CDC are chemicals including DEET and picaridin.

Soybean oil is another natural ingredient showing promise for repelling bugs. A study published in the July 2002 *New England*

Journal of Medicine reported that the best non-DEET competitor featured a 2 percent soybean oil repellent.

FDA Attacks

The FDA is attacking a compounding pharmacy for stating that "bio-identical hormones are identical to hormones found in the human body."

This is only a definition, not a claim. So the truth is a lie and a lie is the truth if from big brother. No matter what will cause healing or cure, it can't be stated in America unless it is an FDA approved drug.

Well, what's it all about? It is war on natural medicine!

According to Jonathan V. Wright, M.D. (April 2008 *Nutrition and Healing* 1-915-849-4605, $74 per year) the best and least used treatment for Alzheimer's is Lithium: "Lithium is a common mineral element in the same family as sodium and potassium. It is not a drug and not patentable.

"Low-dose lithium is brain-protective. It increases the number of brain cells in older individuals. It appears to be better than anything, drug or otherwise, for Alzheimer's.

"Low dose lithium is safe for everybody. Consider it at once if you have a family history of Alzheimer's disease, senile dementia, Parkinson's disease, or any other neurodegenerative disease."

Dr. Wright recommends 10 to 20 milligrams of lithium aspartate or orotate.

CHAPTER 15

Hormone Balance for Men and Women

Your Brain is Related To Your Sex Life

What does your brain and your sex life have in common? It's testosterone. There are ways to increase testosterone as we get older. Testosterone decreases with age.

This causes an avalanche of other problems. Testosterone is truly the elixir of youth

With the exception of health enthusiasts, few people are even aware of the great importance of testosterone in total health and this certainly includes most doctors. Of course the trouble is that the line between the natural hormone and the synthetic or steroids, which are illegal, is blurred. This may be on purpose to keep natural hormones out of the mental awareness of the people.

The pharmaceuticals consider hormones to be their domain not least of which is testosterone. But they deal in synthetics or steroids which they extract and sell as prescription drugs.

This blurring and confusing of steroids with natural hormone has worked with the people and most doctors. Pharmaceuticals are masters of deceit. They create confusion that they channel in their favor.

Yes, it is psychological propaganda and confusion. Anything that we lose as we age needs to be replaced if possible. I can think of nothing more important than testosterone.

When natural testosterone is not replaced with age, men's testosterone gets so low that their bodies can't make much estrogen at all. In both sexes the body makes estrogen by converting testosterone to estrogen. I have written about testosterone 5 percent cream from a compounding pharmacy. This is what I use, but there are other non-prescription precursors that produce natural testosterone.

The sex hormones come from cholesterol and the pharmaceuticals are trying to stamp out cholesterol under the pretext of heart health. It is commerce and actually the lowering of cholesterol is extremely negative for heart health. And the doctors won't come off of this anti-cholesterol phobia.

The first cause of skyrocketing cholesterol is insulin imbalance. Testosterone and the other sex hormones, estrogen, and progesterone are produced out of cholesterol as well as the sex hormone precursors DHEA and androstenedione.

As we age we seem to get insulin resistant, causing overweight and diminished testosterone and DHEA levels. Pharmaceuticals don't say much about insulin because any honest insulin studies lead to the subject of the high U.S. consumption of fructose corn syrup and the health hazard it is causing, resulting in a pandemic of diabetes.

Sugar makes high insulin and medical problems. Low insulin correlates with higher DHEA levels and higher testosterone levels and normal cholesterol levels.

Well, we started with the direct relationship of the brain and sex life or sexual potency. I, like most people, think of testosterone as it relates to enhanced sex life, or diminished sex life if testosterone is low. But Dr. Jonathan Wright in his October 2008 newsletter *Nutrition and Healing* states that testosterone levels are directly related to cognitive function.

He says, "The sex part is important, no doubt, but who cares about sex if you can't remember who you're with or what you're doing with her?"

Dr. Wright says that natural, "testosterone replacement for

men is extremely important for significantly reducing the risk of Alzheimer's disease and cognitive decline."

Also "higher serum (natural bio-identical) estrogen levels in women in their 60s are directly correlated with lower incidence of Alzheimer's in those same women decades later.

"Testosterone for men and estrogen (that's real, bio-identical estrogen—not horse estrogen as used in conventional medicine) for women is very protective for the entire cardiovascular system, including the blood supply to the brain." (End of Dr.Wright quotes).

Seniors, we all need to be aware of declining levels of nutrients and hormones with aging. We need iodine, DHEA, Co- Enzyme Q10, glutathione, etc. Above all, let's try not to become insulin resistant. Watch all sugars or sweetners, especially fructose corn syrup. It is more dangerous to the people than a standing army.

Testosterone and Male Anti-Aging

Aging men can improve their physical, sexual, and psychological health with testosterone supplementation using natural androsome cream.

Male menopause (andropause), a syndrome related to aging, may begin in men as early as their 40s. Andropause consists of physical, sexual, and psychological symptoms that include sexual dysfunction, weakness, fatigue, reduced muscle and bone mass, anemia, diminished reproductive abilities, depression, anxiety, irritability, insomnia, memory impairment, and reduced cognitive function.

In short, males have a mid-life crisis caused by declining levels of the dominant male hormone, testosterone. As testosterone levels begin to go down around age 40 to 50, male virility begins a gradual decline attended by distinct and visible health problems.

Testosterone levels in women are about 1/10th that of men and theirs declines with age also. In both men and women, sadly, their levels of estrogen begin an unnatural rise at the same age that testosterone levels begin to decline. It's a double negative to lose testosterone and gain estrogen.

This excess estrogen begins to show in unnatural weight gain, especially around the mid-section. More to the point, female and male menopause seem to be triggered at the same time as natural testosterone and progesterone decline.

It is now becoming known, mostly from the research and clinical practice in other countries, that natural testosterone offers important life-saving benefits ranging from relief from loss of libido to absolutely serious protection against heart disease, osteoporosis, and prostate enlargement.

In men, natural testosterone minimizes risk factors for heart attack by reducing cholesterol and triglycerides, angina, athero-sclerosis, high blood pressure, and helps normalize blood clotting and obesity. Natural testosterone and natural progesterone should be used by both men and women. But women should use only 1/10th as much testosterone.

Natural testosterone (androsome) is protective for both sexes. Testosterone use is focused on vascular disease and libido enhancement.

There is a second part to testosterone therapy. It's called L-Arginine and it makes the perfect magic duo. L-Arginine opens blood vessels, increasing blood flow.

It is directly linked to the relief of atherosclerosis, diabetes, blood clots, infection, heart failure, and especially impotency. It specifically applies to erectile dysfunction in men and low libido in men and women.

Any or all of the following predict sexual impotency in men: They are aging, high blood pressure, arteriosclerosis, depression, anxiety, insomnia, and especially prescription drugs.

Few people know or understand the toxic nature of prescrip-tion drugs and how they accumulate in the body. L-Arginine, an amino acid, along with testosterone (androsome), is a natural therapy for your heart, your cardiovascular system, and erectile dysfunction.

Though many feel the magic benefits of androsome and

L-Arginine very quickly, some may experience benefits over a month or several months.

The High Risk of Synthetic "Estrogen Therapy"

We have reported to readers for several years the very high risk of Hormone Replacement Therapy (HRT). In the United States, hormone replacement therapy or HRT simply means prescription for synthetic estrogen.

So-called "estrogen therapy" has probably caused the death of more women than wars have killed men. And it's still going on with the blessings of the FDA in spite of years of scientific evidence that HRT causes cancer and heart attacks.

Can the death of tens-of-thousands of women on the altar of conventional medicine be justified any more than the murder of young men in war? Just because HRT is called medical treatment does not in any way or under any pretense justify murder. And the fact that both the women and their doctors are ignorant of what they are doing does not change the charge of murder.

Realism is rare in our Orwellian world. "My doctor told me," may be the most seductive and dangerous phrase in the English language for our moms. God bless 'em, why won't they read? It's only their life!

Inexpensive and simple modalities cry out for prevention and reversal of cancer. Most doctors will not agree to any treatment unless it is prescribed drugs. Follow the money!

Balanced nutrition plus natural progesterone supplementation not only can prevent cancer but actually reverses pre-malignant cells as well as diagnosed cancer.

What is balanced nutrition? As applied to cancer, it is natural complexes such as folic acid (folate), vitamins A, C, and E. These should not be isolated synthetics. Folate is crucial in prevention and returning early cancer cells back to normal cells. Folic acid is also very important in protecting blood vessels against the damage from the amino acid homocysteine that leads to heart disease.

Synthetic estrogen "therapy" leads to estrogen dominance and cancer. What can be done to counteract this? The answer is natural progesterone.

Natural progesterone is for both men and women as it produces no secondary sex characteristics. It causes neither feminization nor masculinization. Its most basic role appears to be as a precursor of the natural production of virtually all of the other adrenal steroids, including cortisone, androstenedione, testosterone and the natural estrogens estone, estrodiol, and estriol.

Synthetic estrogen causes obesity, blood clots, strokes, epilepsy, uterine fibroids, fibrocystic breast, breast and uterine cancer, PMS, osteoporosis, depression and emotional breakdown, water retention, decreased libido, irregular and/or excessive menstrual bleeding, craving for sweets, and excess deposition of fat, especially around the hips and thighs.

Natural progesterone, on the other hand, has many positive benefits for both males and females of all ages. These include water metabolism (especially excretion of water and sodium), increasing libido, balancing thyroid function, assisting in the metabolism of fat for energy, helping cells use oxygen, and stimulating bone growth.

Natural progesterone does reverse osteoporosis causing the actual regeneration of bone tissue. There is absolutely no doubt about this. Progesterone protects against strokes and excellent studies show natural progesterone to be a heart protective. Progesterone inhibits atherogenesis—the formation of cholesterol, containing plaque in the arteries, which eventually can lead to the blockages that cause a heart attack.

In summary, the cancer crisis is directly related to unopposed synthetic estrogen dominance. The answer is balanced nutrition and especially natural progesterone for males and females at all ages.

CHAPTER 16

Cancer Treatment

Cancer is a Fungus!
A Revolution in Tumor Therapy

Tullio Simoncini, M.D., says that conventional oncology produces a 2 percent or 3 percent survival rate, far less than the medical propaganda claims.

In fact the conventional treatments of surgery, chemotherapy, and radiation cause great destruction to the body's natural immune response, resulting in early death with far greater suffering. And he adds that drugs have become the fourth main cause of death after infarction, cancer, and apoplexy.

Even though most establishment doctors know the futility of conventional oncology, intellectual conformity keeps them in line and looking the other way. A conformist attitude which arises out of contemporary medical training has an unbelievable hold on the minds of most doctors. Conformity has been seeded and cultivated resulting in numbing any ability to think, to analyze and to open the mind towards anyone who puts forth something that does not harmonize with the system.

Doctors in their white coat ivory towers would be the last to believe their "medical" and social indoctrination. They are not only victims of the system, they are its servants.

Anyone can quickly evoke a negative response from their doctor by suggesting a nonconventional therapy no matter how powerful and self evident its efficacy.

In America, cancer is money. Cancer is an industry, and have you noticed that there is far more money in "searching for a cure" than finding one.

Medical authorities know that given the very high cancer mortality figures, it is normal that fear of such a devastating disease pervades all of society, producing a wide-spread feeling of impotence and resignation, notwithstanding that health institutions always do their utmost to convince the population about the merits of official scientific cancer research and the remarkable results that have been reached.

Dr. Simoncini says that cancer is an infection (a fungi) not the allopathic premise that genetics is the cause. All conventional cancer therapies are based on a presumed genetic degeneration which in turn is responsible for the unregulated reproduction of cells. Sodium bicarbonate he says, is effective and fatal to cancer.

At the beginning of the 1900s, one person out of 100 died of cancer. Today it is one out of three, and in a few years it will be two people out of three who die of cancer.

Dr. Simoncini says that cancer patients continue to die powerless, among the most atrocious suffering caused by state-sanctioned oncological therapies, conned by a perverse information system that is supported by lies, false information and deceit. It is all about pharmaceutical, state funded, controlled studies and research that wraps the medical enigma in an aura of mysticism above the intelligence of the people and the doctors.

Such is modern awe and wonder and empty fraud. It's a system. It's money and it's a bet that the people and their oncologists will never understand anything about this dark system.

I am willing to believe that few people will ever question modern oncology idiocy. I for one would try Dr. Simoncini's simple and successful bicarbonate of soda therapy without hesitation. It is too simple to ever be officially accepted that cancer is a fungus and it is quickly and successfully treated with mainly bicarbonate of soda.

Dr. Simoncini says that many doctors are using his therapy. Dr. Simoncini's website is: *www.cancerfungus.com.*

The following is a comprehensive outline from Dr. T. Simoncini's book and other sources.

The Politics of Cancer: Keep 'em Sick!

As usual, America's abandonment of the world's best natural anti-cancer medicine has nothing at all to do with science, but everything to do with politics and profits.

If vitamin D were a cancer drug made by Pfizer®, the American Cancer Society would likely be pushing it as the next "miracle" drug and calling for everyone to be put on the drug. But since it's a nutrient that cannot be patented, and can actually be manufactured for free by exposing your skin to natural sunlight, the entire U.S. cancer industry now laughingly pretends that vitamin D supplementation offers no benefits.

Each day that the American Cancer Society, the AMA, the FDA and others in conventional medicine refuse to acknowledge the benefits of vitamin D supplements for preventing cancer, they lose yet more credibility and slip one step closer towards global humiliation and irrelevance. It is difficult to imagine how anyone from conventional medicine can show up at a health event and say, with a straight face, that they're doing everything they can to fight cancer when in reality they are willfully ignoring a prevention medicine that really works: Vitamin D.

It's simple, safe, and virtually free, and it has no negative side effects, requires no patent royalties, and is available right now to everyone. If there were ever a cancer prevention strategy to get behind, this is it!

The people in the cancer industry, if they had any sense, should be leaping out of their chairs, fumbling over each other in a mad rush to the press conference podium to announce their support for vitamin D.

And yet what do we hear in the United States? Complete apathy. It's as if these people somehow believe that a vitamin manufactured by the human body itself has no role in human nutrition.

The depth of blind ignorance at work here is mind boggling. Someone should actually start a psychological study of the people in the cancer industry to figure out how their minds can work that way. It should be called, "The Madness of Crowds and the Illusion of Cancer Treatments in Western Medicine."

Benefits of Baking Soda for Getting Rid of Cancers

We are going back to medical basics with the application of the least expensive, safest and perhaps most effective cancer medicine there is.

Sodium bicarbonate has been on many cancer patients' minds this past year. It has not been easy though to get to Rome or even contact Dr. Tullio Simoncini for treatment. And doctors willing to give bicarbonate I.V.s are not on every corner, so it's been somewhat frustrating to have something so simple and effective remain elusive.

Though we have known that oral intake of sodium bicarbonate will have the "Simoncini" effect on oral, esophagus, and stomach cancer, we have not focused at all on the systemic effect of bicarbonate taken orally. Every cancer patient and every health care practitioner should know that oral intake of sodium bicarbonate offers an instant and strong shift of blood pH into the alkaline.

So strong is the effect that athletes can notice the difference in their breathing as more oxygen is carried throughout the system and as more acids are neutralized. The difference can be stunning for those whose respiration is labored under intense exercise loading.

This tells us to take very seriously the oral use of bicarbonate for cancer treatment no matter what other treatment is used. If the amounts of H+ and CO_2 exceed the capacity of hemoglobin, they affect the carbonic acid equilibrium, as predicted by Le Chatelier's Principle or the quantitative treatment in terms of equilibrium constants.

As a result, the pH of the blood is lowered, causing acidosis. The lungs and kidneys respond to pH changes by removing

CO_2, HCO_3^- and H^+ from the blood.

When one reads my thesis on different medicinal substances one has to always remember that I am a protocol man who does not support single shot cures for anything. With the publication of today's chapter on sodium bicarbonate and maple syrup, sodium bicarbonate slips securely into the number three spot right behind magnesium chloride and iodine.

Each of these three substances effects directly onto basic human physiology in a way most pharmaceutical drugs do not. When used together we have a super threesome that will inexpensively go far to resolving many of the physical and even some of the emotional problems we and our children face.

And if you have not made the connection, please note that all three of these substances are used in emergency rooms and intensive care wards and they do commonly save lives every day with their inherent healing powers.

All cancer sufferers (and in fact, every chronic disease patient) should hold clearly in mind that pH is the regulatory authority that controls most cellular processes. The pH balance of the human bloodstream is recognized by medical physiology texts as one of the most important biochemical balances in all of human body chemistry.

pH is the acronym for "Potential of Hydrogen." In definition, it is the degree of concentration of hydrogen ions in a substance or solution. It is measured on a logarithmic scale from 0 to 14. Higher numbers (above 7.2) mean a substance is more alkaline in nature and there is a greater potential for absorbing more hydrogen ions. Lower numbers indicate more acidity with less potential for absorbing hydrogen ions.

Our body pH is very important because pH controls the speed of our body's biochemical reactions. It does this by controlling the speed of enzyme activity as well as the speed that electricity moves through our body; the higher (more alkaline) the pH of a substance or solution, the more electrical resistance that substance or solution holds.

Therefore, electricity travels slower with higher pH. If we say something has an acid pH, we are saying it is hot and fast. Alkaline pH on the other hand, biochemically speaking, is slow and cool.

For example, you all know about the Kentucky Derby. Well, race horses have an acid pH which makes them nervous and jumpy. They will run themselves to death. So why is the Kentucky Derby in Louisville? It's because the soil pH is acid and perfect for race horses.

On the other hand, horses which feed on grass grown on alkaline soil (higher pH) are laid back, slow, and gentle. They are the opposite of race horses.

Race horses burn out quick, and the same is true with people who are highly acidic. Body pH level changes are intense in the profundity of their biological effects. Even genes directly experience external pH.

pH differentially regulates a large number of proteins. Increased oxidative stress, which correlates almost exponentially with pH changes into the acidic, is especially dangerous to the mitochondria, which suffer the greatest under oxidative duress.

Epigenetics, which may now have begun eclipsing traditional genetics, commonly describes how factors such as diet and smoking, rather than inheritance, influence how genes behave. The following chapter comes after 100 pages of text in the "Yeast and Fungi Invaders" section of *Winning the War on Cancer* book.

Please note that sodium bicarbonate taken in water alone will have a powerful effect on the entire body physiology because of the instant shift into alkaline pH levels.

Bicarbonate can be taken frequently throughout the day with half teaspoon amounts, though for long-term use lower doses are safer. For cancer patients, initial use should be heavy and frequent to force a greater shift because smaller pH shifts can actually stimulate cancer growth.

Common sense knowledge speaks loudly about cancer for

Candida patients avoiding glucose. This is similar to the common sense of pilots who know to pull back on the stick to pull out of a dive.

That works until you approach the speed of sound and at that point all the pulling in the world will not work. You have to push the stick forward and do what instincts scream not to do. Several died trying until Chuck Yeager pushed that stick forward and became the first man to break the speed of sound.

Bicarbonate Maple Syrup Cancer Treatment
(International Medical Veritas Association)

The bicarbonate maple syrup cancer treatment focuses on delivering natural chemotherapy in a way that effectively kills cancer cells but significantly reduces the brutal side effects experienced with most standard chemotherapy treatments.

In fact, so great is the reduction that the dangers are brought down to zero. Costs, which are a factor for the majority of people, of this particular treatment are nil.

Though this cancer treatment is very inexpensive, do not assume it is not effective. The bicarbonate maple syrup cancer treatment is a very significant cancer treatment every cancer patient should be familiar with and it can easily be combined with other safe and effective natural treatments. This cancer treatment is similar in principle to Insulin Potentiation Therapy (IPT).

IPT treatment consists of giving doses of insulin to a fasting patient sufficient to lower blood sugar into the 50 mg/dl. In a normal person, when you take in sugar the insulin levels go up to meet the need of getting that sugar into the cells.

In IPT they are artificially injecting insulin to deplete the blood of all sugar then injecting the lower doses of toxic chemo drugs when the blood sugar is driven down to the lowest possible value. During the low peak, it is said that the receptors are more sensitive and take on medications more rapidly and in higher amounts.

The bicarbonate maple syrup treatment works in reverse to IPT. Dr. Tullio Simoncini acknowledges that cancer cells gobble up sugar—so when you encourage the intake of sugar it's like sending in a Trojan horse. The sugar is not going to end up encouraging the further growth of the cancer colonies because the baking soda is going to kill the cells before they have a chance to grow.

Instead of artificially manipulating insulin and thus forcefully driving down blood sugar levels to then inject toxic chemo agents, we combine the sugar with the bicarbonate and present it to the cancer cells, which at first are going to love the present. But not for long!

This treatment is a combination of pure, 100 percent maple syrup and baking soda and was first reported on the *www.CancerTutor.com site.* When mixed and heated together, the maple syrup and baking soda bind together. The maple syrup targets cancer cells (which consume 15 times more glucose than normal cells) and the baking soda, which is dragged into the cancer cell by the maple syrup (being very alkaline) forces a rapid shift in pH, thus killing the cell.

The actual formula is to mix one part baking soda with three parts (pure, 100 percent) maple syrup in a small saucepan. Stir briskly and heat the mixture for five minutes. Take 1 teaspoon daily, (suggested by Cancer Tutor) but one could probably do this several times a day.

"There is not a tumor on God's green earth that cannot be licked with a little baking soda and maple syrup." That is the astonishing claim of controversial folk healer Jim Kelmun, who says that this simple home remedy can stop and reverse the deadly growth of cancers.

His loyal patients swear by the man they fondly call Dr. Jim and say he is a miracle worker.

"Dr. Jim cured me of lung cancer," said farmer Ian Roadhouse. "Those other doctors told me that I was a goner and had less than six months to live. But the doc put me on his mixture and in a couple of months the cancer was gone. It did not even show up on the x-rays."

Dr. Jim discovered this treatment accidentally somewhere in the middle of the last century when he was treating a family plagued by breast cancer. There were five sisters in the family and four of them had died of breast cancer. He asked the remaining sister if there was anything different in her diet and she told him that she was partial to sipping maple syrup and baking soda.

Since then, reported by a newspaper in Asheville, N.C., Dr. Jim dispensed this remedy to more than 200 people diagnosed with terminal cancer and amazingly he claims of that number, 185 lived at least 15 more years and nearly half enjoyed a complete remission of their disease.

When combined with other safe and effective treatments such as transdermal magnesium therapy, iodine, vitamin C, probiotics, and other items like plenty of good sun exposure, pure water, and clay treatments we should expect even higher remission rates.

It is very important not to use baking soda which has had aluminum added to it. The Cancer Tutor site reports that Arm and Hammer® does have aluminum but the company insists that is not true. One can buy a product which specifically states it does not include aluminum or other chemicals (e.g. Bob's Red Mill, Aluminum-Free, Baking Soda).

Sodium bicarbonate is safe, extremely inexpensive and unstoppably effective when it comes to cancer tissues. It's an irresistible chemical, cyanide to cancer cells for it hits the cancer cells with a shock wave of alkalinity, which allows much more oxygen into the cancer cells than they can tolerate.

Cancer cells cannot survive in the presence of high levels of oxygen. Studies have already shown how manipulation of tumor pH with sodium bicarbonate enhances some forms of chemotherapy.

"The therapeutic treatment of bicarbonate salts can be administered orally, through aerosol, intravenously, and through catheter for direct targeting of tumors," says oncologist Dr. Simoncini. "Sodium bicarbonate administered orally, via aerosol or intravenously can achieve positive results only in some tumors, while others—such as the serious ones of the brain or the bones—remain unaffected by the treatment."

The maple syrup apparently enables and increases penetration of bicarbonate into all compartments of the body, even those which are difficult or impossible to penetrate by other means. These compartments include the central nervous system (CNS), through the blood-brain barrier, joints, solid tumors, and perhaps even the eyes.

IPT makes cell membranes more permeable, and increases uptake of drugs into cells. The maple syrup will make tissues more permeable, too. It will transport the bicarbonate across the blood-brain barrier and every other barrier in the body for sugar is universally needed by all cells in the body.

The essence of IPT is that it allows cancer drugs to be given in a smaller dose, far less toxic to normal cells, while building up lethally toxic concentrations in cancer cells. Both IPT and bicarbonate maple syrup treatments use the rapid growth mechanisms of the cancer cell against them.

Dr. Jim did not have contact with Dr. Simoncini and did not know that he is the only oncologist in the world who would sustain the combining of sugar with bicarbonate. Dr. Simoncini always directs his patients to dramatically increase sugar intake with his treatments, but has never thought to mix the two directly by cooking them together.

Because his treatments depend on interventionist radiologists who insert catheters to direct the bicarbonate as close to the affected area as possible, or physicians willing to do expensive intravenous treatments, I pushed bicarbonate up into the number six slot in the IMVA cancer protocol. With the discovery of Dr. Jim's work, bicarbonate comes back into our number three spot right behind magnesium chloride and iodine.

That number three slot for a brief time was held by hemp oil containing THC. The great advantage that maple syrup and bicarbonate treatment has over hemp oil is that it is legal, thus easily obtainable.

The two together, backed by a solid protocol of other nutritional substances, make winning the war on cancer almost a certainty.

When using these substances it is safer to change one's vocabulary and not say one is treating and curing cancer. Far better to conceptualize that one is treating the infectious aspect of cancer, the fungus and yeast colonies, and the yeast-like bacteria that are the cause of TB.

Dr. Simoncini says that, "In some cases, the aggressive power of fungi is so great as to allow it, with only a cellular ring made up of three units, to tighten in its grip, capture and kill its prey in a short time notwithstanding the prey's desperate struggling. Fungus, which is the most powerful and the most organized micro-organism known, seems to be an extremely logical candidate as a cause of neoplastic proliferation."

pH of the blood is the most important factor to determine the state of the microorganisms in the blood.

"Sodium bicarbonate therapy is harmless, fast, and effective because it is extremely diffusible. A therapy with bicarbonate for cancer should be set up with a strong dosage, continuously, and with no pauses in cycles in a destruction work which should proceed from the beginning to the end without interruption for at least seven or eight days.

In general, a mass of two to four centimeters will begin to consistently regress from the third to the fourth day, and collapses from the fourth to the fifth," says Dr. Simoncini.

There are many ways to use sodium bicarbonate and it is a universal drug like iodine and magnesium chloride. Raising pH increases the immune system's ability to kill bacteria, concludes a study conducted at The Royal Free Hospital and School of Medicine in London.

Viruses and bacteria that cause bronchitis and colds thrive in an acidic environment.

To fight a respiratory infection and dampen symptoms such as a runny nose and sore throat, taking an alkalizing mixture of sodium bicarbonate and potassium bicarbonate will certainly help. The apple cider vinegar 1/4 teaspoon and 1/4 teaspoon baking soda taken two times or more a day is another treatment, as is lemon and baking soda, or lime and baking soda formulas.

Perhaps honey could be substituted for maple syrup for those who live in parts of the world where maple syrup is not available, but to my knowledge no one has experimented with this.
—Mark Sircus Ac., OMD

Cancer Tip

Cancer is a sugar junky. Cancers thrive on sugar. Tell people you know who have cancer to avoid all sugar of all kinds especially fructose corn syrup. And avoid it yourself and extend your life and health.

Warning: Almost all commercial foods contain sugar. If we avoid sugar, we will have to work at it in America.

What to do About Cancer Risk

Control your insulin levels. Make certain that your intake of processed foods, carbohydrates, and/or sugars is as close to zero as possible.

■ Get Omega-3 fats from cod liver oil.

■ Take up to 5,000 IUs of vitamin D3 daily.

■ Eat as much fresh raw vegetables daily as you can. Research has shown that if one half of your diet is raw, the probability of no cancer is very high.

■ Maintain ideal body weight.

■ Boil, poach, or steam your foods. Never fry or charbroil.

■ Take iodine daily according to your needs.

CHAPTER 17

Senior Health

Aging is a Drying-Out Disease

For some reason, seniors drink less water as they get older and move less. And since they take so many drugs, this compounds their dehydration, especially with the taking of so many antihistamines.

Antihistamines block hydration leading to acidic blood and the masking of pain. What we mistake as pain and disease is really chronic cellular dehydration.

Seniors do not drink enough water to dilute and dispose of acid waste, greatly contributing to the aging process. Add to this a lack of exercise and acid buildup in the tissues overloading the lymphatic system. Dehydration over time leads to chronic acid/alkaline imbalance (overacidity) causing chronic disease.

Increased water consumption contributes to alkalinity simply by expelling, diluting, and washing out acidity. Health is restored when diet is returned to 80/20 alkaline over acidity coupled with rehydration.

Rehydration by itself causes health miracles but added to an 80 percent alkaline diet, health benefits grow exponentially. The more alkaline in your diet, the more rapid your improvement will be.

Take your daily calcium and keep check on saliva and urine pH. Proper pH balance (7.365 pH) is the foundation for health and restored health. It's a good idea to take a mineral supplement with the eight glasses a day water therapy.

Physiology of Cardiac Output and Aging

The equation is: Heart Rate x Stroke Volume = Cardiac Output. This equation means that decreasing stroke volume results in increasing heart rate, in order to maintain adequate cardiac output.

As Franke (1981) noted, "The really fundamental change affecting the heart and circulatory system over the course of its biological existence is the general decline in its capacity to adapt to physical exertion as age increases. Accordingly, the stroke and minute volumes and the maximal oxygen uptake — which provide a measure of the physical reserve — all decline after the 30th year of life."

An increase in heart rate is brought about by an increase in the production of catecholamines.

If stroke volume decreases, sympathetic dominance must develop in order to maintain cardiac output. Overproduction of catecholamines can go so far as to become toxic to cells because the amount of oxygen available to cells may be insufficient to meet the metabolic requirements, leading to a shift toward anaerobic metabolism.

Stimulated by adenyl cyclase, catecholamines activate phosphorylase in the liver and skeletal muscles. Blood glucose and lactic acid levels subsequently rise, with a decrease in pH and catastrophic drops in tissue ATP levels leading to cellular necrosis (e.g., gangrene and infarction).

By treatment with testosterone we are able to counteract the effect of catecholamines. In accordance with the equation for cardiac output, this means an increase in stroke volume and an improvement of circulation.

Note from Bob: This is a bit medically technical for most of us, but well worth the effort. I re-read several times to sort it out.

There is a lot of talk and print about the negative, costly, and deteriorating state of American conventional medicine. Actually the medical pharmaceutical cartel has nothing to do with health. Health, my friends, is a conscious choice. If we get it we have to pursue it, hence the silent number of alternative physicians.

■ These alternative M.D.s were mostly trained in the big pharma system until they saw the scam and fraud.

■ Testosterone therapy improves oxygen supply which is basic to longevity and stamina. Oxygen supply greatly offsets simple vasoconstriction.

■ There is a direct relationship between physical activity and testosterone production.

■ Hypoxia (deficit of tissue oxygen) and the related anaerobic metabolism is the root of cardiovascular disease (CVD).

Testosterone levels decline gradually, and because it comes on slowly, men and women often accommodate to the symptoms and do not realize how much they have lost.

Testosterone is a principal androgen, or male sex hormone. Even though testosterone is a "male sex hormone," it is important to realize and understand the benefits for women.

One of the group of compounds known as anabolic steroids, testosterone is secreted by the testes but is also synthesized in small quantities in the ovaries, cortices of the adrenal glands, and placenta, usually from cholesterol.

Andropause is the medical term for low-normal levels of natural testosterone. Symptoms of andropause or hypogonadism (male menopause) are:

■ Decreased mental sharpness

■ Decreased energy and strength

■ Decreased muscle and increased fat

■ Decreased sex drive

■ Decreased sensitivity to stimulation

■ Decreased strength of orgasm

■ Decreased erectile function

■ Depression and/or loss of eagerness and enthusiasm

■ Irritability (20 percent to 25 percent of men—heard of "grumpy old men?")

■ Increased risk of cancer (low testosterone levels increase risk)

Men who receive testosterone therapy consequently report that they feel sexier, stronger, and healthier. Testosterone is responsible for the sex drive for both men and women. It is expressed as menopause in women, whereas in men it is expressed as andropause.

Many of these symptoms and disease processes that we come to accept as normal aging are processes that are actually secondary to low testosterone levels and are easily correctable.

In men, hypogonadism is a condition in which the testes produce a less than normal amount of testosterone, the male hormone. When too little testosterone is present, men tend to undergo a drop in sexual desire and performance. They may also experience depression, fatigue, loss of motivation, and osteoporosis.

Andropause (male menopause) symptoms are caused by declining hormones in men. Hormones do not decline because we age—we age because hormones decline.

I have long written that testosterone therapy, exercise, and alkaline pH greatly offsets the American acidic diet and the gradual acidification of the body is attended with terminal illness. Total acid saturation is death.

Chronological aging is a fact. Biological aging is a variable that can be enhanced with testosterone therapy, exercise, and an alkaline pH. This is not rocket science and is available to everyone.

Dehydration

Most seniors (and everybody else) are dehydrated.

Our thirst mechanism begins to fade with age. Even people who are seriously dehydrated will not drink water placed in front of them. I have to consciously drink water myself and you should too.

Unintentional dehydration is a plague on the world. Orthodox medicine's focus is on the solute or solid body, completely ignoring the solvent (water).

Our brain and body are 85 percent water. Water is a nutrient and possesses a dominant metabolic role in all physiological functions of the body. Most of us are not sick. We are thirsty.

The "water cure" is not something the medical establishment is interested in. It is too simple and costs nothing and is available to the whole population.

Dehydration is a primary cause of disease but completely overlooked, or is it just omitted. Drinking more water, six to eight glasses a day, can do miracles for seniors and all ages.

■ Water suppresses the appetite and helps the body metabolize stored fat.

■ Drinking enough water is the best therapy for fluid retention. To get rid of excess water, drink more water.

■ Overweight people need more water than thin people.

■ Water helps maintain muscle tone and helps to prevent sagging skin.

■ Water helps rid the body of waste. Many seniors are constipated. And don't forget to take 1/4 teaspoon of sea salt daily. (Malignant hypertension excepted—see your doctor).

Read the last book by F. Batmanghelidj, M.D., *Obesity, Cancer and Depression.* Call 1-800-759-3999 or 703-848-2333 and access the Water Cure website at *www.watercure2.com.*

Manpower! The Elixir of Youth!

There are drugs and synthetics, but what men over 40 need is testosterone.

Doctors are quick to confuse steroids with natural testosterone. Aging diminishes male testosterone. It can and should be replenished on a consistent basis.

There is 5 percent cream and patches available from compounding pharmacies by prescription. Besides the restoration of sexual power, testosterone therapy is a proven treatment for cardiovascular and circulatory diseases. Testosterone is an element essential for the existence and continuance of life.

The following are quotes and extracts from *Testosterone Treatment of Cardiovascular Diseases* by J. Moller of Copenhagen, Denmark: (Broda Barnes Foundation).

■ There is absolute clinical proof of the positive effects of testosterone on circulation.

■ There is definite improvement in patients with impaired carbohydrate metabolism as shown by a decrease in plasma glucose levels.

■ Dr. Charles D. Kochakian as far back as 1951 demonstrated an improvement in nitrogen balance due to testosterone treatment. This is fundamental for the effect of testosterone on cardiovascular disease (CVD).

■ Testosterone has a cholesterol-lowering effect.

■ Testosterone therapy has an anti-diabetic effect counteracting the effect of insulin resistance and the improvement of retinopathy.

■ W. Meyer Molleringh showed improvement in patients with angina pectoris after injections of testosterone. Treated CVD patients show normalization of ECG abnormalities.

■ Claudication (leg pain) patients had longer walking distances, gangrene healed, and angina pectoris symptoms disappeared after three months of testosterone treatment.

■ The testosterone level correlated negatively with blood glucose levels in all subjects.

■ Aging and the deterioration of biological functions can be greatly and positively modified with ongoing testosterone therapy.

■ There is considerable evidence to support the results observed with testosterone therapy. The theory supported by modern endocrinology, physiology, biology and cardiology, that cardiovascular disease (CVD) must be considered to be the result of a disordered metabolism within the cell. While the natural progress of life cannot be altered, the administration of transdermal testosterone makes it possible to intervene in cases where this progress has become accelerated. The use of testosterone can improve the status of an afflicted circulatory system and has saved thousands of patients from amputation, gangrene, angina symptoms, and disability. Transdermal topical skin application of testosterone cream has saved many lives.

■ The plague of male impotency can greatly be naturally relieved. Women need only 10 percent as much testosterone supplementation as males. Who among us can't rub on a little transdermal cream daily?

Caveat: People with prostate cancer should not use testosterone.

Seniors, Don't Break Your Bones!

You know the story. Old folks fall, break a bone, get pneumonia and then often die. But it shouldn't be!

Researchers have demonstrated that if seniors take their calcium and magnesium plus daily doses of at least 1,000 units of vitamin D3, they can escape the above sequence.

Give yourself three months to build up. Please don't worry about vitamin D3 overload. Many people in the know take 5,000 international units (IU) daily. Health Canada recommends an upper limit of 2,000 IUs of D3 daily.

Want to know the biochemistry of vitamin D3? Science teaches that only plants process photosynthesis, but people do too.

People manufacture nutrition (D3) from the sun. Of course seniors mostly use D3 supplements to get the sun benefit. But bone health is not the only benefit.

The risk of dying with cancer is far, far less with high doses of vitamin D3 daily. Studies have linked a shortage of D3 with such serious chronic ailments as multiple sclerosis, diabetes, heart disease, influenza, Alzheimer's, and schizophrenia.

Unknown to doctors, vitamin D3 is introducing a golden age in medicine, and natural medicine at that. But please don't wait for your doctor as he will be the last to know. By that time, you could be long gone.

The vitamin D3 supplement that I personally use daily is called Advanced D3 Plus™ from Health Resources™, 1-800-471-4007. Vitamin D3 is directly related to public health.

Geography can damn millions to terminal illness. I mean northern latitudes where there is less sunshine to make D3. But northern people can take D3 supplements.

Older ages absorb less, so take more. Also, overweight people require more as do all dark skinned people.

Vitamin D3 acts as a hormone in the body's cells and packs a huge biological punch.

The Canadian Cancer Society became the first major organization in the world to embrace the idea of large-scale population-wide vitamin D3 supplementation to combat cancer.

One study, in the journal *Circulation,* found that those with low vitamin D3 had a 62 percent increased risk of heart failure. And the number is 72 percent lower risk for colorectal cancer if vitamin D3 is at adequate levels.

When the Canadian Cancer Society asked the American Cancer Society to join them in recommending more vitamin D3, it refused.

My prediction: The U.S. pharmaceuticals are hard at work to develop a vitamin D analog (drug). And when they do the government will greatly restrict the potency of natural vitamin D or outlaw it all together with the ruse that vitamin D is a hormone, not a food.

The research is moving fast and the efficacy of vitamin D3 is overpowering. The U.S. medical establishment won't allow it.

Recognizing a Stroke

Neurologists state that if they can get to a stroke victim within three hours, then they can totally reverse the effects of a stroke. The trick is recognizing, diagnosing, and getting to the patient within three hours, which is tough in many cases.

A True Story: Susie is recuperating at an incredible pace for someone who suffered a massive stroke. This is because Sherry saw Susie stumble and asked Susie three key questions — so simple that it literally saved Susie's life. When asked the questions, Susie failed all three, so 911 was called.

Even though she had normal blood pressure readings and

did not appear to be having a stroke, as she could converse to some extent with the paramedics, they took her to the hospital right away. Sometimes symptoms of a stroke are difficult to identify.

Unfortunately, the lack of awareness spells disaster. The stroke victim may suffer brain damage when people nearby fail to recognize the symptoms of a stroke.

Now doctors say a bystander can recognize a stroke by asking these three simple questions:

1. Ask the individual to SMILE.
2. Ask the individual to RAISE BOTH ARMS.
3. Ask the individual to SPEAK A SIMPLE COHERENT SENTENCE.

If he or she has trouble with any of these tasks, call 911 immediately and describe the symptoms to the dispatcher.

After discovering that a group of non-medical volunteers could identify facial weakness, arm weakness, and speech problems, researchers urged the general public to learn the three questions listed above. They presented their conclusions at an annual meeting of the American Stroke Association.

Widespread use of this test could result in prompt diagnosis and treatment of a stroke and prevent brain damage.

Arthritis, a Nutritional Deficiency

The test of Dr. E.M. Pottenger (on cats fed pasteurized milk and cooked meats) as reported in the *American Journal of Orthodontics and Oral Surgery,* Aug. 1946, is an eye opener.

Cats on this diet all developed arthritis before death, but first lost their teeth from pyorrhea and continually suffered from constipation, bone degeneration, stomach and intestinal ulcers, sterility, heart enlargement, liver congestion, and various other changes common to human patients on the same diet.

The point is that pasteurized milk is cooked and is no longer a food. It becomes a dead and a synthetic "food." Yet it is a huge industry and a staple in the American diet.

On the other hand, those who feed infants raw milk soon find out the phenomenal difference in the nutritional effect. Of course, raw milk has almost passed out of existence.

The rest of the story on Dr. Pottenger's cats is that the second generation couldn't reproduce and they died out of existence. Applied to the human race, population control is achieved over time with dead and synthetic foods.

Dr. Agnes Fay Morgan proved that with synthetic vitamin B1, the second generation of her experimental dogs could not reproduce. To induce a population to consume dead and synthetic foods is the most seductive psychological warfare.

Yes, most "advertising" can be defined as psychological warfare. You are induced or persuaded to eat "foods" that destroy mind and body. Any type of persuasion or manipulation that leads one against his health or financial well-being is psychological warfare. Trickery of the mind cannot be otherwise.

The welfare of a nation is based upon the health of its people, and generally good health is based upon nutritional food as nature intended. Every organized food processing business and the government conspires to manipulate the American diet for commerce. The result is that not one in a million knows the difference in a natural and a synthetic food or a natural food vitamin and a synthetic vitamin.

Dr. Royal Lee said in 1953, "Nature produces plant-complexes with known and unknown complements that function synergistically, which in the animal produce the vitamin effect. Just as the chemist cannot create life, neither can he create a complex vitamin: The life element in foods and nutrition. This is a mystery the chemist has never solved and probably never will, and the synthetic vitamins he creates on the basis of chemical formula bear as much resemblance to the real thing as a robot does to a living man, lacking an elusive quality that chemistry cannot supply."

The point is that modern chemistry cannot create food and nutrition. But they can make substances that taste delicious and look delicious but are non-food chemicals in most cases full of transfatty acids and fructose corn syrup.

The taste and the appearance disguises the crime. Synthetic and plastic foods that produce calories and no nutrition can only mean a national crisis of full belly starvation. And when we get sick, the medics administer drugs for malnutrition instead of food.

But there are a few who have caught on to the chicanery and they have deserted doctors, drugs, and the commercial food processors.

Reverse Memory Loss

Reverse your memory loss and senile dementia in the early stages. Even better, take preventive action.

Phosphatidylserine (PS) is the crucial nutrient for the aging mind. It doesn't exist in the average American diet.

Doses of 300 mg to 500 mg per day have shown marked improvement in memory and thinking ability and even reversed early Alzheimer's as well as depression.

Many have quick results but most don't, so commit to at least six months. If you don't commit for six months, don't complain if it doesn't work for you.

Cure Seniors' Brittle Bones, Eliminate Toxins—With Exercise!

Seniors, all the calcium and magnesium in the world won't help your bones unless you exercise. Bone growth or re-mineralization won't happen with calcium and magnesium alone.

Bones grow and become stronger in direct relationship to exercise or stress placed upon them. Bones are living tissue. The more stress or pressure you exert on them, the stronger they grow.

We need daily exercise with our bodies exposed to sunshine as much as possible. Thirty minutes of direct sunlight daily is for total health. Bones love it!

We can walk and lift small weights on our feet and with our hands. Muscle tone means stronger bones. Think of the law of physical motion. "For every action there is an equal and opposite reaction." When you put pressure on your bones by walking, swimming, lifting weights, etc., your bones respond by becoming stronger

Exercise is not an option. It is a must! Exercise stimulates the lymphatic system in the body to help eliminate toxins. Lymphatic drainage is a major function to good health.

Since the lymphatic system has no heart to pump like the vascular system, it can only function by exercise. Exercise does the pumping action to move the fluid and expel toxins.

Please keep this in mind, seniors. I suspect old age feebleness comes mostly from lack of movement and the accumulation of poisons in the body. Walk briskly every day as much as you can.

Practice Deep Breathing

The more you inflate your lungs, the healthier they become. Use the "two for one" method of breathing. That means for every second you inhale you should exhale two seconds.

Deep breathing helps the lymphatic system expel toxins. The lymph system has no pump of its own, although it gathers waste from throughout the body. The lymph glands swell when they are collecting more toxins than they can handle. Lymph glands work better to expel toxins with deep breathing.

Shallow breathing leads to sickness and eventual death. The aging population all have shallow breathing in common. Their resistance is low and they develop colds and flu. The function of the lymphatic system is to purify the blood, produce white blood cells, and eliminate toxins. However, it must pump to do so.

I put sticky notes up all around to remind me to breath deep. Believe me, it's very important.

CHAPTER 18

Controlling Disease and Ailments

Vitamin D3 and Ultraviolet Therapy

If I knew that I had cancer of any kind or any other intractable disease, I would think first about detoxification of my blood.

Life is in the blood. I believe that the benefits of ultraviolet therapy (detoxification of the blood) can be received through massive doses of vitamin D3 daily. Even a short-term loading dose of 50,000 units per day for a week should be considered (under medical supervision.)

It is not toxic, but uninformed people will tell you that it is. The shortest route to blood detoxification would be ultraviolet sterilization. It is also called blood irradiation or photoluminescence.

The alternative doctor draws a small amount of blood, places it for a few seconds under UV light and then re-injects it into the patient. The history of this procedure and its success goes back to the 1920s, according to Jonathan V. Wright, M.D.

Now of course any alternative success which is not under the controlled medical system is forbidden and risks the medical license of those doctors who actually have as their first concern the health of their patients. I myself had photoluminescence treatments and I think they were beneficial to me and others that I witnessed.

The doctor was well aware of the risk from the FDA et al. He would remove his equipment at night from his office in case of a raid.

Let me inject here that doctors or anyone else do not come

into conscious reality until and unless they have inquiring minds and never, never cease questioning the modus operandi of "authority." One must always suspect that money and power motivates authority and the very last thing would be an interest in the welfare of the public.

Now my doctor (can't reveal his name) was savvy about alternative medicine. I would drive a few hundred miles to see him. But like so many intelligent people, he had a black hole in his thinking. He served a Federal sentence for, "failing to file and pay his income tax."

He protested his income tax on the grounds of refusing to "support the Vietnam War." Come now, would any of you have been so foolish? I hope not.

The truth is that the Vietnam War and all wars were and are funded with NOTHING, called fiat. There is no such thing as income tax funding anything.

This is the big deception and my good well-meaning doctor went to jail. How sad!

I said nothing as this subject goes beyond the parameters of conventional thought. He would not have understood that fiat means that there is no payment, only exchange simulating payment.

As long as we believe that fiat is money, we will be grossly deceived. We cannot know reality.

Hypothyroidism or Iodine Deficiency?

We really can't separate hypothyroidism from iodine deficiency. They should be looked at together.

Most of the time hypothyroidism and/or iodine deficiency are unsuspected by doctors and most of them don't test for it. If one has fatigue, depression, weight gain, memory loss, hair loss, muscle cramps, dry skin, decreased libido, cold feet, confusion, delirium, or even heart failure, he/she should suspect hypo-thyroidism and iodine deficiency first. Really nothing could be simpler to diagnose and treat.

Anyone can test themselves for hypothyroidism or iodine

deficiency. Low basal (at rest) body temperature is a prominent indicator of low thyroid function.

Take underarm temperature for three days, before you get out of bed, and figure the average. If you are running as much as one degree or more below 98.6 you can suspect hypothyroidism.

You can request an iodine loading test from your doctor. I would start my iodine test by just rubbing food grade iodine (Lugol's) on a small spot, maybe two inches across on my arm. If the iodine disappears overnight, I would take this to mean an iodine deficiency.

Even if too much iodine is taken it will be excreted.

Iodine has a detoxifying effect on the body. Chances are that most of us have an iodine deficiency. I think that we can assume this because iodine is generally low in agriculture soils everywhere.

Iodine is important for the whole body but it is concentrated in the prostate gland, the thyroid, and breast tissue.

Iodine: Case History on Fibromyalgia

John, age 58, was diagnosed with fibromyalgia two years ago: *"I don't know what happened. One day I was ok and the next day I ached all over and I was tired."*

John saw numerous doctors who prescribed various medications.

"The drugs did not help. I kept telling my doctors 'I wasn't depressed' but they kept prescribing antidepressants. I finally got sick and tired of taking the drugs," he said.

When John saw me, I found his thyroid gland to be enlarged. I ordered an ultrasound of his thyroid gland and blood work and diagnosed him with Hashimoto's disease.

"When I found out I had Hashimoto's disease, I couldn't believe it. I had been seeing many different doctors and they couldn't tell me what was wrong. They kept telling me I needed to be on an antidepressant medication," he said.

After doing an initial history and physical examination, I tested

John's iodine level. John's iodine loading test was found to be low at 45 percent (normal ^90 percent). John was placed on 75 mg of iodine/day along with a complete nutritional program. After 12 weeks of taking iodine, a follow-up 24-hour iodine loading test was now normal at 95 percent excretion. However, he did not feel better.

John was still complaining of fatigue and body aches. Furthermore, John's TSH increased from a baseline of 4 IU/L to 12 IU/L after taking 75 mg of lodoral for 30 days. John had normal T3 and T4 levels. John's endocrinologist placed him on thyroid hormone (Synthroid) for the elevated TSH level.

The Synthroid had no effect on his symptoms. When I saw John, I felt that he may be having an organification problem with the iodine. I explained to him that his cells were unable to effectively utilize iodine.

After placing him on vitamins B2 (100 mg) and B3 (500mg) two times per day, John noticed an immediate improvement.

"With the second dose of the B-vitamins, my head cleared and all my fatigue went away. I felt 20 years younger. I have never taken anything that works that quickly," he said.

John has continued to take iodine (now 50 mg/day) in addition to vitamins B2 (200 mg/day) and B3 (1,000 mg/day). His thyroid antibody levels gradually lowered to normal levels over the next six months. Most importantly, John now feels well.

"I can't believe how much energy I have. Everybody has noticed the difference," he claims.

From the book, *Iodine, Why You Need it and Why You Can't Live Without it,* 3rd Edition by David Brownstein, M.D. Order at 1-888-647-5616 or *www.drbrownstein.com.*

Programmed Cell Death

Our cells, if healthy, are programmed to die a natural death within a certain time. This process is called "apoptosis."

When our cells grow wild and don't die on time, we have cancer. Iodine promotes apoptosis or normal cell death. But the, *"required daily allowance (RDA) is not enough for iodine dependent tissues of the thyroid, breasts, ovaries, uterus, and prostate gland. Daily preventive adult doses range from 6 mg to 50 mg/day for the vast majority of adults. Iodine levels can be measured by checking blood, urine, and/or saliva."*

From Dr. Brownstein's book, *Iodine,Why You Need it and Why You Can't Live Without it,* page 160.

Acidosis

Our bodies are alkaline by creation. We do have a definite need for acid in the stomach to aid digestion, but no other part of the body should be acid.

Paradoxically, what news media medicine advertising calls "acid stomach" (and sells billions of dollars worth of antacids) is in fact low stomach acid. Yes, chances are, if one has gastric acid symptoms, the stomach is low in acid.

Permanent relief can only come with more acid in the form of hydrochloric acid.

Do you want a restored digestion, a normal stomach, and expanded general health? Take about 1/4 to 1/2 teaspoon of sea salt daily in a glass of water. Expect a miracle!!

Email Bob Butts for his free CD on salt and water at *watercure2@comcast.net.* He has invested large sums of money to give away a miracle.

He says that the medical establishment wants sickness to keep money flowing to their coffers. Oh, you don't believe that? And what do doctors and hospitals give the sick patient upon entering the hospital? A very, very high priced salt (saline) water I.V.

Acidosis in the body (excepting the stomach) is a cause of disease unrecognized by medical people. Symptoms of acidosis may take the form of chronic degenerative disease which may include cancer, diabetes, arthritis, emphysema, arteriosclerosis, or heart disease.

As neutralizing alkaline reserves are depleted, the liver becomes increasingly congested and is unable to detoxify. Then the extracellular and intracellular fluids lose their alkalinity causing serious acidosis leading to complicated health problems as above.

The Acidity Theory of Death

Death is the progressive accumulation of acid. The more acid our system is the less available oxygen we have.

First, look at coronary flow being disrupted by acidity-causing atherosclerotic lesions. Blood does not flow symmetrically, as scientists originally believed. Instead, it flows in two opposing corkscrews surrounded by a third corkscrew-like flow.

This combination creates an asymmetrical spiraling flow that is encouraged by the natural curves and bends of human arteries. Lowered pH (acidity) leads to the generation of mechanical forces in blood flow, causing a cardiovascular disease process. Lowered pH increases perfusion pressure and greater contractility of coronary arteries.

Acidity and Oxygen Reserves

Individuals with chronically acidic systems use up oxygen reserves quickly. Alkalinity produces oxygen. Over-acidity leads to toxin accumulation and oxygen depletion.

The body tries to combat excess acidity by trying to neutralize it with oxygen. To do so, it must continually divert oxygen away from its primary metabolic functions and direct it toward the acidic cells and tissues.

This means that as we get more acidity, we have less oxygen and shorter breath. Older people are, of course more acid. Acidity interferes with our electromagnetic currents, creating more acid in the body.

pH and Blood

Blood pH must be in balance (slightly alkaline) so that red blood cells remain separate (not clumping) and therefore can flow into the smallest capillaries to deliver oxygen.

Acid actually strips away the negative charge of red blood cells causing them to clump. This means less oxygen gets to your cells. Acid also weakens red blood cells and they begin to die. We get fewer nutrients and our energy begins to drop. Infectious micro-organisms thrive in low pH or acid environments.

What to do? Use apple cider vinegar for pH balance with your meals. We should also be drinking an abundance of alkaline water. Supplement with alkaline drops as in Alkaline Body Balance™ 1-800-471-4007.

The Calcium Wave—A Miracle For Me!

The calcium wave is so powerful that it may be my most satisfactory research to date. The calcium wave can be your miracle.

Regardless of your health concern, the calcium wave (calcium lactate) can be powerful for you. If it sounds too simple and too cheap, it is. But I'm going to try and overcome that. It is not modern medicine and it is not science. It is simply biochemistry.

Medical journals from around the world, from Scandinavia, Europe, and the United States substantiate the existence and the powerful presence of the calcium wave in protecting the body against infectious disease. The calcium wave cannot be observed with the human eye, but Howard R. Petty, Ph.D., professor of Biophysics at the University of Michigan Health System's Kellog Eye Center, demonstrated that high-speed energy and techniques enabled him to merge his knowledge of physics with cell and molecular biology by using high sensitivity fluorescence imaging with shutter speeds 600,000 times faster than video frames.

High-speed imaging enabled researchers to actually see the movement of the calcium wave. The calcium wave images resembled the movement of a comet across the night sky. What we're talking about here is simply the therapeutic benefits of taking calcium lactate in powder form regularly.

Mark Anderson, in his lecture on the calcium wave, used

two tablespoons of calcium lactate powder in a glass of water. I know that the lack of calcium is conducive to illness and fever at all ages from a teething baby to a mature senior. Ninety-nine percent of our body calcium is in our bones, but it is that one percent that has to do with the pathology of infection and the calcium wave.

This story all takes place within the human cell. For this action to occur we must have a supply of ionic or diffusible calcium (calcium lactate).

The calcium wave sends signals to key players in the immune response. The calcium wave is a stream of calcium ions coming into the cells. As the cell membrane begins to surround its pathogen target, two calcium waves begin to circulate.

When the target is completely surrounded, one wave traveling around the cell's perimeter splits in two with the second wave encircling the phagosome or sac-like compartment. The second wave allows the enzymes to enter the phagosome and finally destroy the target.

The human immune system is miraculous, but it must have the proper raw materials to protect the body from infectious disease—both viral and bacterial—which tends to attack from the outer world, pathogens outside of our skin.

Calcium lactate as ionizable or diffusible calcium: Two to three tablespoons daily, depending on whether it is a small or large person, is the average dose.

Do I think calcium is important to our health? Our parathyroid gland is designed exclusively for calcium utilization; no other gland is dedicated to just one mineral. I use Ultimate Calcium™ from Health Resources™ 1-800-471-4007.

Relief for Parkinson's Disease Symptoms

It begins with slight trembling or shaking, usually in the fingers or one hand. Over time, the tremor worsens and other symptoms such as slow movement, muscle rigidity, and difficulty walking appear.

Doctors prescribe a drug called Sinemet® or other drugs. Of

course, they don't work.

Nerve damage is the problem. Natural products like phosphatidylcholine, silicon, coenzyme Q10, and glutathione are the answer. Informed and alternative doctors use coenzyme Q10 and glutathione (an amino acid) injections specifically for Parkinson's disease.

Dr. Sherry Rogers says in *Total Wellness* that a glutathione injection is an inexpensive and quick reversal, within minutes, of Parkinson's symptoms.

Folic Acid Helps Prevent Parkinson's Disease

Studies with mice show that folic acid may help prevent Parkinson's disease. We have known that folic acid supplementation can prevent birth defects.

Folic acid will also reduce homocysteine levels in adults. High homocysteine levels are an important new marker for heart disease.

Vitamin supplements of B6 and folic acid will help keep levels normal. Folic acid deficiency is also related to cervical dysplasia. Women of childbearing age should have 400 mcgs. of folic acid daily.

The Curse of Gout

Gout usually attacks the joints of the big toe. Uric acid crystals cause gout by depositing in the tissues causing inflammation, swelling, and immobility of the foot. Sometimes it causes severe pain.

Bowel bacteria digests uric acid, preventing gout attacks, but here again, a lot of bulk is required for maintaining sufficient amounts of bacteria. This calls for fiber.

I have never seen a case of gout that blackberry juice or black cherry juice concentrate wouldn't relieve within 24 hours.

How much to take? Several tablespoons full. If you, like most people, feel compelled to "see your doctor," then advise him/her that you want some tetracycline for your gout. It is very effective.

Bleeding Gums

Cyruta is a nutrient that will firm the gum tissue around the teeth. Bleeding gums respond very quickly to four to six tablets of Cyruta daily. Once the bleeding stops, cut the dosage as needed. Cyruta also can be used to dissolve calcium deposits in blood vessels. It seems to support the elastic connective tissues so that calcium cannot be deposited in the blood vessels.

Uterus Fibroid Tumors

Iodine should be considered by every female as a dietary supplement. The ovaries require and store large amounts of iodine. It is the number one deficient nutrient for many, but especially in females. Bleeding is common with fibroid tumors.

Vitamin K, found in chlorophyll complex will many times control the bleeding.

Fibroid tumors usually start to decrease in size after menopause. Don't be in too big a hurry for surgery.

The Chlorophyll Transfusion

Whenever you have a blood-related illness, including loss of blood for any reason, chlorophyll is a transfusion of the most direct type. Chlorophyll actually creates the blood.

If you want an antioxidant to control free radical pathology, you need chlorophyll complex. It is the perfect antioxidant.

The most important component of blood is vitamin K. Without vitamin K, blood leaks. Many people have loss of blood constantly. They probably lack vitamin K to seal off the leaks. Chlorophyll is an excellent source of vitamin K.

Green Tea and Cinnamon

We did it and it works!

Yes, we bought the cinnamon bark and boiled several sticks while brewing green tea loaded with fresh mint leaves. It forces blood pressure down and greatly helps reduce insulin resistance and heads off Type II diabetes. It is a great drink cold or heated.

Let me know how it works for you. Give it a few weeks and keep a check on your blood pressure.

Glaucoma, Cataracts, and Macular Degeneration

Like all other degenerative disease, eye disease is a huge industry. By all definitions it is truly a commercial enterprise. One and a half million cataract surgeries a year generate about $4 billion in gross medical revenue.

The risk of eye disease simply goes up with age. But age is not the only consideration, because all seniors don't have eye disease. Now a great many people do benefit from corrective eye surgery even though there are risks.

Glaucoma is commonly treated with medication to release fluid pressure. Intraocular pressure can even be increased by some prescription drugs such as glycosteroids, tricyclic anti-depressants, nitroglycerin or amylnitrite, a recreational drug.

Drugs have side effects and may do more harm than good. All steroid hormone drugs can cause or advance glaucoma.

Develop the habit of reading all inserts that come with drugs. Tell your pharmacist that you want the original insert then you can evaluate the drug for yourself.

Not all people with eye fluid pressure develop glaucoma, and 25 percent to 30 percent of those who do develop glaucoma have normal eye pressure. Even though there has been great advancement in corrective eye surgery, especially cataract surgery, still some people—4 percent to 6 percent—have negative results. Many do get relief from one symptom but find that others deteriorate and they need follow up laser treatment.

About 25 percent of Americans over age 65 have macular degeneration. The wet form accounts for 90 percent of legal blindness in the United States. Macular degeneration is generally uncorrectable and irreversible especially in later stages.

Started early enough, there may be reasonable hope. No use getting into the medical science of these three eye diseases. You know if you have vision impairment and deterioration.

If you smoke, your risk is at least threefold. Smoking compounds vasoconstriction.

Also, prolonged exposure to artificial light damages the eyes and infrared light from incandescent lighting contributes greatly to cataract formation.

What can we do on our own that would benefit us along with modern medicine?

Natural foods are the best source for eye protection. This includes whole-natural foods with additional whole-food complex supplements. We recommend live foods only.

Caveat: Do not use synthetic supplements as they can and do create biochemical imbalances that will aggravate your deficiencies. Be warned that the word "natural" on a label means nothing.

Forget about the concept of "high potency." Biochemical effects are not related to potency.

If you can't switch to totally whole-natural food complexes all at once, then start phasing in today. Get a juicer and start juicing carrots, cucumbers, celery, apples, pineapples, etc., as fresh as you can get them.

Get the whole-food complex Garden Variety™, which includes carrot juice powder, beet juice powder, barley grass juice powder, broccoli powder, tomato powder, cabbage leaf powder, and kelp. This is live food and easy to take. It has not been heated but vacuum dried to preserve maximum live nutrition.

The eyes have to have vitamins A, C, and E. People who have adequate levels of these vitamins do not develop cataracts nearly as often. Vitamin C is 30 times higher concentrated in the lens of the eye than in the blood. Vitamin B-complex is very essential to eye health. Raw food complexes are rich in live enzymes which are necessary for biochemical reactions.

Minerals are very important, particularly zinc. Zinc is vital to eye nutrition because it is essential to vitamin A metabolism. Zinc should be in a natural complex with other minerals. The herb bilberry is associated with helping eye ailments due to high blood pressure and nearsightedness. It strengthens capillary walls and improves delivery of blood and oxygen to the eyes.

Avoid sugar and all sugar substitutes except honey, raw brown sugar, or Stevia (a natural herb sweetener). Sugar and products made from white flour are deadly to your health and your eyes. Stop using these poisons no matter what your age.

Food is Medicine and Medicine is Food

Understanding this is the elixir of life. This is anathema to modern medicine which implies that sickness is a drug deficit. Oh, yes, most doctors would laugh at this but nevertheless, their total approach to sickness implies that human sickness is drug related and drug dependent. Food is not only for safety but for the essence of life.

Ginkgo Biloba

I have written about ginkgo biloba many, many times, just as I have vitamin D3. But it takes repetition to drive a truth home.

I know that most of our readers are seniors, and I also know that most of you have something in common—sludging blood that comes with aging. Blood sludging means simply bad circulation leading to memory loss and general mental deterioration.

But what I worry about is heart attack and stroke. Don't we know that the very first thing cardiologists do for a heart attack is give the patient blood thinner? Ginkgo is a super natural blood thinner and I consider it to be important in preventing a heart attack or stroke. It has a 5,000 year history and is widely prescribed in Europe.

Wipe Out Herpes With BHT

"Prevent it if you don't have it. Get rid of it if you do. This amazing substance also improves health and beauty of skin, helps prevent cardiovascular disease and cancer, and extends lifespan." Quoted from *Wipe Out Herpes With BHT,* by John A. Mann and Steven W. Fowkes.

Caveat! Though the research shows BHT to be every word quoted above, it is not a medicine. It cannot be prescribed as a medicine, and by Food and Drug rules and regulations, it cannot be anything more than BHT (butylated hydroxytoluene), a common food preservative and can only be sold as such.

Please, please keep this in your mind: I don't care if it's dirt, if it is wonderful for me and you and is nontoxic—unlike drugs which are toxic—it should be used. Can you guess who doesn't want you to know about this?

What is BHT? It is a common food preservative that is widely used to prevent rancidity in fat-containing foods such as breakfast cereals, baked goods, potato chips, pork sausage, peanut butter, instant potatoes, and other commercially processed and prepared foods.

The FDA (Food and Drug Administration) has approved its use in amounts up to 0.02 by weight of the food product since 1947. The typical daily intake in the U.S. is estimated to be about 2 mgs.

Although it is a completely synthetic substance it is a much safer compound than many substances in everyday commercial foods. It has vitamin-like effects on humans and animals.

I take it and I give it to my dog. Keep in mind that health is derived from non-drug, non-toxic food, and therapy no matter what the pharmaceutical drug high priests say and try to get you to believe through their mass advertising (propaganda).

If BHT is widely used to prevent rancidity, it follows that it neutralizes rancidity. Then what are the possibilities and potentials to prevent a widespread inability of people to digest fats and neutralize rancidity and fermentation?

The chemistry is conclusive or commercial food processors could not use BHT to extend shelf life and thereby massively increase their profits. Rancidity is very carcinogenic and toxic to health. It is a major concern because the slightest rancid taste causes immediate rejection of any food.

Rancidity is biochemical deterioration and it is easily identified by both smell and taste. It follows that anti-rancidity would greatly enhance the purification of the stomach environment and have the effect of supplementing stomach acid. Most of us, particularly seniors are low on stomach acid.

If BHT will preserve food from rancidity, it will preserve people from the effects of rancidity. Wait, I don't think that you are supposed to know this! What if BHT acted like an enzyme and helped the digestive system by prolonging digestive time, giving the body longer to digest and assimilate?

Well, this is crazy! We are only talking about a common food preservative. And maybe we are talking about unintended benefits. People who are not programmed have no trouble at all following this.

How Safe is BHT?

"The only apparent long-term effect from the small amount of BHT (2 mgs or so daily) that most Americans get is a statistical reduction in the incidence of gastrointestinal cancer since this preservative first came into commercial use in 1947. In experiments with animals, larger doses have reduced the incidence of many kinds of cancer by much greater amounts. On the basis of animal experiments and other evidence, scientists have made conservative estimates that 250 mgs of BHT daily could reduce the human cancer rate to less than half of what it is today (1983). It could similarly lower the occurrence of heart attack and stroke. Animals that are given large daily doses of BHT live up to 50 percent longer than normal and maintain youthful characteristics throughout most of their lives. In the early 1950's, Denham Harman, at the University of Nebraska, extended the lifespan of mice by 50 percent with large doses of BHT.

"Although BHT is a synthetic compound, it bears many chemical similarities to some naturally occurring nutrients and seems to have vitamin-like activities in the body. For the past five or ten years (before 1986 when this was written) thousands of people have been taking 250 mgs to 3000 mgs of BHT daily for its protective and life-extending properties and have noticed many

health improvements and no significant side effects. There have been a few reports of short lasting lightheadedness within a half hour after taking BHT on an empty stomach. For this and other reasons, we suggest taking it with meals." (End quote from *Wipe Out Herpes With BHT,* by John A. Mann and Steven W. Fowkes).

There are no figures available (up to 1983 when this book was written) about acute toxicity in humans from extremely large amounts of BHT, even though BHT is not classed by the FDA as anything more than a food preservative.

BHT and Herpes Simplex

Herpes is an infection (that due to the decaying morality and free love in America) is spreading like wildfire. Genital herpes (type 1) and type 2 oral herpes both disappear in about the same amount of time when BHT is taken.

Herpes Simplex sometimes manifests into sores and blisters but most often is latent and harmless but can reappear at any time. BHT has been better than 99 percent effective in eliminating herpes of all types.

Herpes generally implies sexual misconduct but this is only part of the picture. Millions of people have latent herpes virus hangover from mumps, measles, chicken pox, common cold sores, or fever blisters. It is also possible to contact the herpes virus and not have any symptoms for years, and then have your first flare-up because of stress, decreased resistance, or other biochemical changes.

I personally had herpes simplex in the form of shingles while in college at age 19. Shingles ravages people at all ages and is particularly severe for seniors. BHT is the answer to a really bad infection.

"In addition to BHT's free-radical-scavenging properties, BHT causes the induction of various liver enzymes which meta-bolize carcinogens. Many potent carcinogens exhibit lowered activity, sometimes markedly, when co-administered with BHT. Also, several kinds of cancer have been linked to the herpes

*virus; skin cancer with HSV-1 and cervical cancer with HSV-2.
If herpes virus can lead to cancer, as most researchers now
believe to be so, BHT can give triple protection against cancer
by 1) destroying lipid-containing viruses, 2) scavenging free
radicals, and 3) inducing anticarcinogenic enzymes, all at the
same time."* Quoted from *Wipe Out Herpes With BHT.*

Cervical cancer is a killer of thousands of women yearly.
Recently we discussed the high effectiveness of Cataplex F
with this virus. Now we add BHT. Actually, susceptibility to
herpes is an indicator of one's state of health.

Heart Disease

Large doses of BHT as used in treating herpes could result
in a sharp decrease in cancer, heart disease, and stroke.

I feel sure that most readers of this *Letter* no longer believe that
coronary heart disease is directly related to a high-cholesterol diet
as most doctors still believe. In fact it is a medical religion and
in gross error.

Later studies hold that free radicals damage the cells of artery
walls and cause the cells to reproduce wildly, forming a tumor-
like cluster that breaks through the artery wall and attracts
calcium and cholesterol from the bloodstream.

Calcium and cholesterol accumulate to form the plaque that
clogs the arteries and cuts off the flow of blood causing a heart
attack. It is only through inhibiting the free radical process that
heart disease can be avoided or stopped once it starts.

In cancer and heart disease there is the free radical problem
of cells reproducing wildly. BHT arrests this process and the
body reverts back to apoptosis or normal cell death. This is a
Mother Earth health phenomenon that costs practically nothing.

Also, vitamin D promotes normal cell death (apoptosis) thus
preventing cell mutation in heart disease and cancer. Needless
to say institutional medicine promotes neither BHT nor vitamin D.
Can you guess why?

Herpes, Difficult for
The Immune System

The immune system has a difficult time getting at the herpes virus because of a lipid fatty coating that camouflages its proteins.

This lipid coating is one of the main reasons why there is no effective treatment for herpes (outside BHT). But, this fat coating of the virus draws BHT making it very effective in destroying herpes.

There are two ways that BHT inactivates lipid-containing viruses. First, BHT disrupts the virus' lipid cloak, leaving it naked and vulnerable to attack by the immune system.

Second, it removes binding proteins that viruses use to penetrate cell membranes. What matters is that 250 mgs or more of BHT daily causes all symptoms of the disease to disappear within several days to a week.

Should BHT be discontinued the symptoms may or may not return. Even serious cases in remission may go for very long periods symptom-free.

If dosage is maintained symptoms do not recur. What could be simpler? The extended benefits of BHT are helping to prevent the major causes of cancer, heart disease and stroke, and in extending lifespan.

A curious thing is that in stubborn cases of herpes there is a problem of poor fat absorption or insufficient dietary fat. For BHT to be absorbed it must first dissolve into fats or oils.

Who promotes these "low-fat and no-fat" diets? I have long thought that the "people" in the inner sanctum of the system know all variables of health and fiat finance. They created the system and we are their toys.

"The free radical defense system is so fundamental to life, aging, and disease, that the addition of a synthetic free-radical scavenger to the system can have profound effects." (Quoted from the book *Wipe Out Herpes With BHT* by John A. Mann and Steven W. Fowkes).

The majority of this article came from this book.

What to do?

How do we avoid political authoritarianism? How do we get natural immunity no matter what we are exposed to?

Conventional medicine is disguised authoritarianism with the broad power to physically assault the population with needles of inoculation by the pharmaceuticals, the federal and state governments, down to the school boards and teachers.

Viral or bacterial infection is preceded by low ionized calcium. Likewise, peak immunity comes with ionized calcium in the tissue cells.

We need four critical nutrients to build natural immunity at all ages. They are: Calcium lactate, vitamin D3, vitamin F, and vitamin C complex.

In the event of sickness (fever or infection), there should be a check for blood calcium levels (ionized calcium). It is a rare event for a doctor to check this or to even be aware of it.

To repeat again: There are two very important signs or indicators of any sickness or disease. They are high body temperature and low ionized or blood calcium.

Likewise, low body calcium comes with high body temperature. Very simple, but important to remember.

Calcium is needed in the stomach. I like calcium lactate powder because it is easy to get enough of it dissolved in water. Second, we need vitamin D3 to absorb calcium from the gut into the bloodstream. Third, we need vitamin F (fatty acid) to move calcium from the blood into the cell tissue. Fourth, we need C Complex to arm the phagocites for war with and on pathogens. This foursome is dynamite nutrition and unless an insufficient amount of these four is taken, immunity is certain in the midst of any viral or bacterial epidemic.

This is the basis of complete immunity. This, however, does not exclude good food and nutrition as most of you understand it.

Vitamin D3 is the only effective vitamin D to make this foursome system work. This system of immunity will work if enough is taken.

Chemical Death From "Natural Causes"

In America the worse health becomes the more profitable it is.

How is health made worse and more profitable? The answer is Big Pharma, creating expanding markets for non-diseases.

The more "need" for drugs created, the greater the toxemia resulting in silent chemical death for millions. Drugs are poison or they wouldn't be drugs.

Hundreds-of-thousands of doctors plus the pharmaceuticals equal credibility for chemical poisoning with drugs. And you thought you died from "natural causes!"

Assault upon the people with drugs and immunizations is chemical warfare and the most deadly form of terrorism. It's murder incorporated under the wrapper of medical treatment — yes, "health care."

Can educated automatons execute millions of people with chemical poison and not know what they are doing? Such is the Machiavellian nature of a mind control system devoid of common sense.

Symptomology triggers the created desire for drugs when in truth all so-called diseases are crises of toxemia. In medical orthodoxy, it's not about prevention and cure. It's about quieting symptoms with drug poison. I highly recommend the book, *Toxemia Explained,* by J.H. Tilden, M.D. $29.95 from Health Resources™ (1-800-471-4007).

There is a very limited supply of this valuable book.

Sometimes Drugs?

I don't like drugs or the people who make them, but there may be wisdom in taking some drugs on occasion and for short periods. Antibiotics of the tetracycline class, particularly minocycline and doxycycline, have produced dramatic results in cases of very resistant arthritis.

In a University of Nebraska Medical Center study, patients with rheumatoid arthritis were treated with 100 mg of minocycline twice a day for a year. Fifteen patients of a 23 minocyclin group had 50 percent improvement.

These studies also show some anti-inflammatory benefit in addition to antibacterial activity. We are talking pain relief here as well as treatment for fibromyalgia and chronic fatigue syndrome.

Many people have occult or sub-clinical inflammation that these antibiotics could help. But I have never seen an allopathic doctor prescribe probiotics to follow any and all antibiotic therapy.

This doesn't have to be a big deal, just drink whole buttermilk with antibiotics.

Ulcers: It is now known that bacteria that can cause ulcers respond well to the tetracycline antibiotics.

Joint Replacement: Orthopedic surgeons always recommend antibiotics as pre-medication for almost any small intervention, such as dental work. You're in deep trouble if you have knee joint replacements and they get infected—that many times calls for emergency surgery.

Of course, if we have peak immunity this is a non-issue, but should we take the chance?

CHAPTER 19

Heart Health

From Cardiovascular/Cardiology News: How Much Salt is Safe?

An increasing body of evidence indicates that we should reduce the amount of salt in our diet. The American Medical Association (AMA), the American Heart Association (AHA), the American Dietetic Association (ADA), and the National Institutes of Health have begun a campaign to cut the salt intake of Americans by one-half.

Sounds like another big pharma/government propaganda campaign to feed big pharma more bodies. When that many government agencies all come out against salt, you had better get the debate from the other side.

What crass and base nonsense! And yes, the American people will follow and their general health will enter a new downhill direction.

Heart doctors already have their patients off of salt. This started 60 years ago. The following salt information was taken from the book *Obesity, Cancer, and Depression,* by F. Batmanghelidj, M.D. It is a discussion about sea salt, not refined table salt.

As a rough rule of thumb, Dr. Batmanghelidj recommends 1/4 teaspoon of sea salt per quart of water. Exceptions are those with kidney failure or other medical reasons which call for a doctor's consultation.

The government agencies listed above, who set the direction for our "medical welfare," should take note that when we get sick and land in the hospital, they immediately give saline (salt) I.V. drip with 0.9 percent concentration of salt. This figure translates to 9 grams of salt per liter of water.

However, it is prudent to take only a third as much salt on a regular daily basis. And these silent injections of salt cost the insurance companies more than gold costs.

The following are direct quotes from Dr. Batmanghelidj's book: *Salt: Some of its Hidden Miracles:* "Salt has many functions other than just regulating the water content of the body." Here are some of its additional important functions in the body:

■ Salt is a strong natural antihistamine. It can be used to relieve asthma: Put some on your tongue after drinking a glass or two of water. It is as effective as an inhaler, without the toxicity. Remember, you should drink one or two glasses of water before putting salt on the tongue.

■ Salt is a strong anti-stress element for the body.

■ Salt is vital for extracting excess acidity from inside the cells, particularly brain cells. If you don't want Alzheimer's disease, don't go salt free, and don't let them put you on diuretic medications for long!

■ Salt is vital for the kidneys to clear excess acidity, passing it into the urine. Without sufficient salt in the body, the body will become more and more acidic.

■ Salt is essential in the treatment of emotional and affective disorders. Lithium is a salt substitute used in the treatment of depression. To prevent suffering from depression, make sure you take some salt.

■ Salt is essential for preserving the serotonin and melatonin levels in the brain. When water and salt perform their natural antioxidant duties and clear toxic waste from the body, essential amino acids, such as tryptophan and tyrosine, will not be sacrificed as chemical antioxidants. In a well hydrated body, tryptophan is spared and gets into the brain tissue, where it is used to manufacture serotonin, melatonin, indolamine, and tryptamine— essential antidepressant neurotransmitters.

■ Salt is a vitally needed element in the treatment of diabetics. It helps balance the sugar levels in the blood and reduces the need for insulin in those who have to inject the chemical to regulate their blood sugar levels. Water and salt reduce the extent of secondary damage associated with diabetes.

■ Salt is vital for the generation of hydroelectric energy in all of the cells in the body. It is used for local power generation at the sites of energy needed by the cells.

■ Salt is vital to the communication and information-processing of nerve cells the entire time that the brain cells work-from the moment of conception to death.

■ Salt is vital for the absorption of food particles through the intestinal tract.

■ Salt is vital for clearing the lungs of mucous plugs and sticky phlegm, particularly in asthma, emphysema, and cystic fibrosis sufferers. Salt makes mucus fluid loose and ready to "disconnect" —by changing the physical state of its structure (the process is called charge-shielding).

■ Salt on the tongue will stop persistent dry coughs; water will enhance this effect.

■ Salt is vital for clearing up catarrh and sinus congestion.

■ Salt is vital for the prevention of gout and gouty arthritis.

■ Salt is essential for the prevention of muscle cramps.

■ Salt is vital to preventing excess saliva production to the point that it flows out of the mouth during sleep. Needing to constantly mop up excess saliva indicates a salt shortage.

Major osteoporosis is the result of salt and water shortages in the body. More than 20 percent of the salt reserves of the body are stored in the shaft of the long bones, giving them their strength. When the diet is short of salt, the stored salt in the bones is released to osmotically balance the content of salt in the blood.

Enhanced External Counterpulsation (EECP)

Enhanced External Counterpulsation (EECP) is a non-invasive therapy that is very safe and relieves angina in most cases. It helps restore blood flow to the heart and improves collateral circulation.

This therapy is not new but not known. We investigated. A well-known cardiologist told me, "We don't promote it." Can you tell why?

It is available in 300 clinics in the U.S . Each treatment takes one hour and 35 treatments are recommended.

Medicare will pay upon your doctor's evaluation. Of course, be prepared for the doctor to try to sell you on bypass surgery. These treatments cost about $200 each if you have to pay for them yourself.

When you call the clinic near you, ask them to send you the video on EECP treatment by Larry King—he had the treatment.

Even if you have had bypass surgery but still have angina, you are a candidate for this therapy.

Bypass the Bypass

Since heart disease is the number one American killer, then bypass surgery ranks right at the top in number of operations performed for any one disease. Without a doubt, heart operations rank at the top as the most expensive.

What Americans need to know is how to bypass the bypass surgery. What can we do to clean our arteries before and after a heart attack? Since the main symptom of a heart attack is death, we need to focus on prevention.

The solution to treatment and prevention for many Americans has been oral chelation (pronounced key-lay-shun). If you have heard of chelation at all, it is probably in connection with cleaning out clogged arteries.

There are many claims now that chelation therapy may reverse the effects of arthritis, cancer, stroke, osteoporosis, glaucoma, mental toxicity, heart attack, senility, and gangrene.

Our modern diet for sure leads to the formation of plaque in our arteries, diminishing blood circulation, leading to hardening of the arteries and many complications and death. Chelation therapy helps reverse artery pathology.

In recent years, many people with no symptoms of artery or heart disease at all are taking chelation therapy intravenously or orally as a preventative measure and purely for life extension. Oral chelators consist of nutritional pharmaceuticals, including the amino acid **EDTA.**

The heart is one of the fastest self-healing organs in the body. Even after the development of serious heart disease, we can do wonders with the proper nutrition.

This may be the time in your life to get serious information about chelation therapy.

High Cholesterol

The best doctors that I know will write a prescription instantly for a statin drug, i.e. a drug to lower cholesterol. The cholesterol myth is a monument to the lies, deceit, and fraud of the pharmaceuticals.

The cholesterol myth proves that super fortunes can be built on the sale of products based on medical myths. This has absolutely nothing to do with medicine or the treatment of disease.

It is commerce, pure and simple. It is crime, incorporated. The cholesterol myth is so well established and so completely accepted by doctors that there is almost no inquiry into this crime of commerce.

Organized propaganda can force feed the public mind any myth they can imagine. Crime becomes legitimate after it is generally accepted by the people. And the longer a crime has been accepted as legitimate or legal, the harder it is to challenge.

Cholesterol drugs are bad for human health. They destroy CoQ10. They complicate general health in many ways. They cost the American people billions-of-dollars annually.

The cholesterol myth is based on the Lipid Hypothesis created by Ancel Keys in the 1950s. The Lipid Hypothesis is a theory that saturated animal fats and cholesterol in our food raise cholesterol levels in the blood. Then the theory goes that high blood cholesterol causes atherosclerosis leading to obstruction of blood vessels of the heart, resulting in coronary heart disease.

The pharmaceuticals saw trillions of dollars of profits. Who can say that the pharmaceuticals didn't create the flawed studies that led to the cholesterol profit empire that we have today.

You may call it a "science" of fraud. This reversed the American diet of good Omega-3 fats to the consumption of liquid vegetable oils and margarine, substituting for coconut oil and animal fat that did our ancestors so well.

Well, as profits skyrocketed, deaths from heart disease and cancer did too.

What is cholesterol? Cholesterol is actually a heavyweight alcohol with a hormone-like structure that behaves like a fat, being insoluble in water and in blood.

Cholesterol has a coating compound called a lipoprotein, which makes it water soluble so it can be carried in the blood. As we will see, cholesterol plays a critical role in body chemistry.

We need our cholesterol. To suppress it with cholesterol drugs is to create degenerative disease.

The Benefits of Cholesterol: From the book *Eat Fat, Lose Fat,* by Mary Enig and Sally Fallon:

■ Your body uses cholesterol to make hormones that help you deal with stress and protect against heart disease and cancer.

■ Your body needs cholesterol to make all the sex hormones, including androgen, testosterone, estrogen, progesterone, and DHEA.

■ Your body uses cholesterol to make vitamin D, vital for the bones and nervous system, proper growth, mineral metabolism, muscle tone, insulin production, reproduction, and immune system function.

■ Bile salts are made from cholesterol. Bile is vital for digestion and assimilation of dietary fats.

■ Cholesterol acts as an antioxidant, protecting us against free radical damage that leads to heart disease and cancer.

■ Cholesterol is needed for proper function of serotonin receptors in the brain. Since serotonin is the body's natural "feel-good" chemical, it's not surprising that low cholesterol levels have been linked to aggressive and violent behavior, depression, and suicidal tendencies.

■ Mother's milk is especially rich in cholesterol and contains a special enzyme that helps the baby utilize this nutrient. Babies and children need cholesterol-rich foods throughout their growing years to ensure proper development of the brain and nervous system.

■ Dietary cholesterol plays an important role in maintaining the health of the intestinal wall. This is why low-cholesterol vegetarian diets can lead to leaky gut syndrome and other intestinal disorders.

■ Finally, the body uses cholesterol to repair damaged cells. This means that higher cholesterol levels are actually beneficial.

Meyer Texon, M.D., a well-known pathologist at New York University Medical Center, points out that indicting fat and cholesterol for hardening the arteries is like accusing white blood cells of causing infection, rather than helping the immune system to address it.

Fact: Deaths from heart disease and all other causes increased 11 percent for each 1 percent drop in cholesterol, according to a 30-year follow-up of the famous Framingham Study. Do the American people know this? No, because the American Heart Association and the National Heart, Lung, and Blood Institute published in the journal *Circulation* the reverse of the above fact.

Yes, believe it or not! And the fact is that for women low cholesterol is more dangerous than high cholesterol. Another fact is that when people maintain low levels of cholesterol in their blood over long periods of time with statin drugs, their risk of death from all causes will increase.

CHAPTER 20

Gastro-Intestinal, Stomach, and Colon Health

Why You Need Hydrochloric Acid

Hydrochloric acid (HCl) is absolutely essential for life! Thus, reduced quantities foretell illness no matter what your age.

HCl starts a disturbing decline after age 40, but it gets worse. Research has shown over and over that, on average, at age 50 there is only 15 percent of the amount of HCl present as at age 25. And 35 percent of all individuals over age 65 do not secrete any hydrochloric acid at all. Therefore, a gastric acid deficiency is the most common condition after age 50. This is a serious health concern!

The pharmaceuticals have seized upon the body's conflicting signals to make multibillions in profits. Here is why: When the body is low on hydrochloric acid, we have symptoms of "heartburn" or "acid indigestion" when, in fact, we are short on hydrochloric acid. But the pharmaceuticals promote antacids by the ton under every name imaginable for the supposed malady of acid indigestion.

Pumping antacids as a palliative for acid indigestion temporarily soothes the symptoms. Prolonged taking of antacids provides no alleviation of the functional problem of low stomach acid. In fact, extended low or no hydrochloric acid masked by antacids can lead finally to stomach cancer.

So-called acid indigestion is a serious malady experienced by millions of people. The major symptom is "heartburn" and/or acid indigestion. Other symptoms may be heart palpitations, short windedness, flatulence and belching, or acid reflux. Complications of low HCl are that the pancreas is influenced.

Proper amounts of HCl increase the quality and quantity of pancreatic secretion. A deficiency of potassium is caused by low or no hydrochloric acid leading again to cancer. **So the symptoms of "heartburn" or acid indigestion are saying to us that we have low stomach acid, not too much!**

HCl keeps us alive by maintaining proper alkaline/acid balance. HCl becomes alkaline after its vital job in the digestive process is done. Eight essential amino acids, two vitamins and 15 minerals are dependent on proper HCl for absorption. Vitamin B12 and folic acid simply will not be absorbed from food sources without the correct amount of HCl in the stomach. Therefore, adequate HCl levels greatly reduce tissue acid waste buildup.

Even proper alkalinity so necessary and so fundamental to health is dependent on normal hydrochloric acid production. HCl is the only acid the body makes and ironically alkaline/acid balance is dependent upon sufficient stomach acid. So again, low HCl is a serious concern not to be covered over with commercial antacids.

All nutritional deficiencies occur with low or no HCl. This is a powerful fact!

Silica

The most important mineral to the health of the intestinal tract is organic silica. Silica is an extremely important mineral to the health of connective tissue formation. It seems to be a key nutrient in the prevention of atherosclerosis.

Many researchers now believe that it is the loss of silica in the connective tissue, not cholesterol deposits, that is primary in the prevention of cardiovascular disease. Silica actually dissolves calcium carbonate deposits in the tissues.

Death Begins in the Colon

Death really begins in our diet but the problems show up in the colon. Everyone needs a practical knowledge of colon health. It's about as serious as any health concern that anyone can have.

Colon health affects total health. We need to burn this into our minds.

According to the noted British researcher, Dr. Dennis Burkitt, at least 10 of our most serious diseases are directly related to a lack of sufficient fiber in the diet. These are: Heart attacks, diverticular diseases, appendicitis, cancer of the colon, hiatal hernia, varicose veins, hemorrhoids, diabetes, obesity (big stomach bloat), and constipation.

Aging compounds colon disease because of our soft food diet and lack of exercise. Primitive people had none of these diseases because of their high raw food diet and thus fiber containing diet.

There is no limit to the amount of fiber that the body can handle. The more fiber, the better the health. We can't have a primitive diet because it is simply not available. We have to supplement with daily fiber. This is very simple but serious and basic to health.

Better Sleep:
No Light, Sleep Tight

Would you like to improve the quality of your sleep? Well, here's a suggestion for you—cover the lights on your alarm clocks, VCRs, TVs, etc... that are glowing while you are sleeping.

These light sources may be interrupting a restful, peaceful sleep and affecting your body. I read that it would be best to have a very dark room and your body may rest better when there is no light. My wife and I covered the lights in our room and there was a dramatic improvement in our sleep patterns.

Also, for very restful sleep, take two beCalm'd™ capsules at bedtime. You won't believe how rested you will feel the next morning.

Snore No More!

We got this tip from a health care practitioner in reference to reducing snoring: "Eat a wedge of lemon before you go to bed at night." I have had an overwhelming, positive response with this simple, but very effective technique. It would be common to think that when we consume citrus that the citrus would remain an acid. Lemon after being metabolized by the body, ends up in an alkaline state. The end results of the lemon metabolism in the body results in a substance that will help reduce acidity, which I have found may, in fact, be the primary cause for snoring.

Fun, Fast Facts!

■ **Cleaning liquid that doubles as bug killer...** If menacing bees, wasps, hornets, or yellow jackets get in your home and you can't find the insecticide, try a spray of Formula 409®. Insects drop to the ground instantly.

■ **Easy eyeglass protection...** To prevent the screws in eyeglasses from loosening, apply a small drop of Maybelline® Crystal Clear nail polish to the threads of the screws before tightening them.

■ **Balm for broken blisters...** To disinfect a broken blister, dab on a few drops of Listerine®... a powerful antiseptic.

■ **Headache pain...** Did you know that drinking two glasses of Gatorade® can relieve headache pain almost immediately— without the unpleasant side effects caused by traditional "pain relievers."

■ **Burns...** Colgate® toothpaste makes an excellent salve for burns.

■ **To clear up a stuffy nose...** Before you head to the drugstore for a high priced inhaler filled with mysterious chemicals, try chewing on a couple of curiously strong Altoids® peppermints. They'll clear up your stuffed nose.

■ **Achy muscles from a bout of the flu?** Mix 1 tablespoon of horseradish in 1 cup olive oil. Let the mixture sit for 30 minutes, then apply it as a massage oil, for instant relief for aching muscles.

■ **Sore throat...** Just mix 1/4 cup of apple cider vinegar with 1/4 cup of honey and take 1 tablespoon 6 times a day. The vinegar kills the bacteria.

■ **Cure urinary tract infections...** Alka- Seltzer®. Just dissolve two Alka-Seltzer® tablets in a glass of water and drink it at the onset of the symptoms. Alka-Seltzer® begins eliminating urinary tract infections almost instantly— even though the product has never been advertised for this use.

■ **Skin blemishes...** Cover the blemish with a dab of honey and place a Band-Aid® over it. Honey kills the bacteria, keeps the skin sterile, and speeds healing. Works overnight.

■ **Toenail fungus...** Get rid of unsightly toenail fungus by soaking your toes in Listerine® mouthwash. The powerful antiseptic leaves your toenails looking healthy again.

■ **Heart disease and cancer...** Researchers from Harvard, no less, have shown that we can cut heart disease and cancer in half with nutrients and turn the p53 cancer gene back to normal with simple carrot juicing.

■ **Carpet outgases...** Volatile organic compounds (vocs) that contribute to the total load of toxins. This leads to the genetic changes producing cancer, allergies, arteriosclerosis, and other diseases. There are more than 200 chemicals that outgas from the average carpet, almost guaranteeing disease. In one test, a piece of carpet was placed in a jar with mice overnight. The mice were found dead in the morning.

■ **Aw, nuts!** *The Archives of Internal Medicine* (June 24, 2002) showed that men who ate nuts at least twice a week lowered their risk of general coronary heart disease by 30 percent because of those good nut oils. Oh boy! Bring on the almonds, walnuts, and the macadamias.

■ **A smallpox vaccination...** Is a live vaccinia virus that reproduces at the site of inoculation and it is transmissible to other people.

■ **Vitamin A...** Is unrivalled as an anti-infective and anti-cancer vitamin.

■ **Potatoes...** Like whole wheat, can support life indefinitely, if eaten baked instead of mashed.

■ **Bananas, too...** Can be used as a single food containing everything needed by the human body.

■ **Nail biting...** Stops in children when supplemental calcium is supplied.

■ **Cold sores and fever blisters...** Are specific signs of low calcium. Adding vitamin F with five grains of calcium lactate will produce a reversal in two or three hours.

■ **Tooth decay...** Is pure and simple malnutrition.

■ **For diarrhea...** In children (or anybody), use boiled milk or blueberries, collinsonia root, and blackberry concentrate. For travelers' diarrhea like Montezuma's Revenge, take 2 teaspoons of whole apple cider vinegar once or twice a day with a glass of water.

Index

Notes:

Notes: